JOSEPH BRANT

Chief of the Six Nations

Born: 1742—Died: 1807

JOSEPH BRANT

Chief of the Six Nations

by Clifford Lindsey Alderman

Julian Messner, Inc.   New York

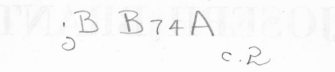

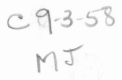

Published by Julian Messner, Inc.
8 West 40 Street, New York 18

Published simultaneously in Canada
by The Copp Clark Publishing Co. Limited

Printed in the United States of America

Library of Congress Catalog Card No. 58-10925

To those descendants of Joseph Brant's people
in New York State who still fight to preserve their
reservation from the white man

Chapter 1

It was not quite dawn when Joseph Brant awoke in the camp on the shore of Lake George. Around him he heard excited voices and the hurried tramp of feet. Sitting up, he peered into the darkness. In the direction of the tent that was General William Johnson's headquarters, he could see torches flaring smokily.

Joseph reached out and shook his friend Ohrante, the young Onondaga warrior who was sleeping beside him.

"Ohrante!" he called. "Wake up! Something has happened!"

His friend stirred and sat up sleepily. "What is it, Thayendanegea?" he asked, using Joseph Brant's Indian name.

"I don't know. Perhaps the French are coming. Let's go over to Warraghiyagey's tent and see."

He spoke in the Mohawk tongue, which Ohrante could understand because the languages of all the tribes of the warlike and powerful Six Nations were much alike.

By Warraghiyagey he meant General William Johnson, the white settler of the Mohawk River Valley, whom the Indians all loved and respected. Because Johnson always treated them kindly, helped them in their troubles, understood their ways, and spoke their language, the Mohawks had adopted him into

7

their Nation. In this summer of 1755 he was in command of the army of provincial soldiers and Indians that had pushed northward through the wilderness from Albany toward Crown Point on Lake Champlain, where his scouts reported the French enemy lay encamped after advancing south from Canada.

Now both Indian boys were on their feet. To dress they had only to slip on their moccasins, since they had slept in the breechcloths that were their only other clothes in the hot weather. They picked up their muskets, strapped on the belts that held powder horn and bullet pouch, threw their blankets over their shoulders to keep off the chill of the approaching dawn, and raced toward General Johnson's tent.

Others had reached it ahead of them. The light of the torches flared on the painted faces of Mohawk, Oneida, Onondaga, Cayuga, Seneca, and Tuscarora warriors, bronzed, black-eyed, crafty, and cruel, with their heads shaved save for their scalp locks, which glistened with bear grease. There were provincial soldiers too—the New England troops the Indians called Bostonians.

They were gathered in a circle about three men. One was Colonel Ephraim Williams, who was at the head of the provincial troops. The other two, roughly dressed, were wild-eyed and panting as they talked to Colonel Williams, gesturing excitedly. Joseph Brant and Ohrante pushed forward, craning their necks.

The flap of the big tent opened and a tall, dignified figure in the scarlet and white uniform of a major general in the British Army of His Majesty George III came through it. General Johnson was still buckling on his sword as he advanced toward the center of the circle. Gold lace gleamed dully on his three-cornered cocked hat.

He spoke to the colonel: "What is it, Williams?"

"The French surprised one of our wagon trains at dusk last night, sir. These men escaped and made their way here."

Johnson turned to the wagoners. "You left Fort Lyman yesterday?"

"Yes, sir," one of the drivers said. "We were heading north for your camp." He had to stop a moment to catch his breath. "An enemy force fell on us from the rear."

"Could you tell how large the force was?"

"A big one, sir!" the wagoner panted. "French and Indians."

"Going north or south?"

"North—headed for your camp, General."

"What happened to the train?"

"The enemy smashed the wagons and killed the other drivers and the oxen. We were up at the head of the train and got away into the woods."

The dawn was coming up fast now. Beyond General Johnson's tent Joseph Brant could see the placid surface of the lake and the misty, broad backs of the mountains surrounding it.

Johnson spoke to Colonel Williams. "You're to take five hundred of your men south to engage the enemy." He gazed around the circle. In the Mohawk language he said, "Where is Teoniahigarawe?"

The war chief of the Six Nations, a Mohawk whom the English settlers called King Hendrick, came into the center of the circle. His face, for all its ferocity, was lined and wrinkled, and his scalp lock was white. He moved with the halting step of an old man.

"You and your braves will go with Colonel Williams, Teoniahigarawe," Johnson said. He looked about the circle again. "Whiting?"

Lieutenant Colonel Nathan Whiting stepped forward and saluted.

"You will lead five hundred more men north," the general said. "This French force came from Crown Point and circled our camp, hoping to surprise us with an attack from the south. If any escape after Colonel Williams meets them, they will retreat north toward Crown Point. Your detachment can thus intercept and destroy them, Whiting."

The old chief, King Hendrick, gave a grunt of disapproval. He picked up a stick and broke it in half. Then he gathered up several sticks in a bundle and tried to break them, but could not.

"One stick is easily broken, Warraghiyagey," he said to Johnson. "Many together are strong. Five hundred Bostonians are not enough."

Johnson thought for a moment, then replied, "Very well, Teoniahigarawe. I will send the whole force of a thousand Bostonians under Colonel Williams."

The old chief grunted again. "It is not enough, Warraghiyagey. It is true that if they are to be killed it is too many, but if they are to fight and win it is not enough."

But General Johnson shook his head and King Hendrick had to be satisfied with a thousand New England troops to go with his warriors.

The whole camp was astir now as officers began to bark orders. The smoke of many fires spiraled into the gray light of the early morning as breakfasts were cooked and hastily eaten.

Seated before their own fire as they ate cakes of corn meal moistened with water from the lake and baked on flat stones, Joseph Brant and Ohrante talked of what had happened.

At length the Mohawk boy became thoughtful. Then he said, "Teoniahigarawe is right. It is like the bundle of sticks that could not be broken. Many together are strong. That is why other tribes fear the Hodenosaunee." He was speaking of the Six Nations. "It is because our six tribes are bound together in one great league that we have beaten our enemies on the warpath. If all the tribes in America were united, perhaps the Indians would be as mighty as the English."

It was something Joseph Brant had often thought of before. Perhaps it was because his own Indian name meant "Two-Sticks-of-Wood-Bound-Together," or "Strength."

Ohrante looked surprised. "But surely you do not doubt that Warraghiyagey knows what is best, Thayendanegea."

"No," the young Mohawk replied quickly. "Oh, no, I do not doubt that. He must have a good reason for not sending more than a thousand Bostonians with us to meet the French."

He did not want his friend to think he did not trust the army's commander. General Johnson was his hero. He was very proud that the white man had married his pretty sister Molly and taken her to live at his great stone mansion, Mount Johnson, on the Mohawk River below the village of Gane-gahaga, which the white settlers called the Upper Castle of the Mohawks.

If it hadn't been for Warraghiyagey, he reflected, he would not be here at Lake George at all, the youngest warrior in the Six Nations. . . .

When the messenger had arrived at Ganegahaga carrying the huge war belt of white and purple wampum which summoned the people to a war council of all the Six Nations at Mount Johnson, thirteen-year-old Joseph had announced he would join the warriors and take the warpath against the French. His mother had been alarmed; his stepfather, Carrihogo, had scowled and said he was too young. And his two older brothers, warriors themselves, had laughed scornfully. It had been War-raghiyagey who had convinced them. . . .

Breakfast over, the Indians began to assemble near General Johnson's cannon. Just as Joseph and Ohrante reached the spot, old King Hendrick climbed slowly up on a gun carriage, raised his hand for silence, and addressed his warriors with fierce pride in his voice.

"Brothers, we of the Hodenosaunee are the most ferocious fighters in all America! The hearts of the White Jackets will quail when they see their enemies, the Iroquois, as they call us. As for the Algonquin allies of the French—the Abenakis and Montagnais"—and Hendrick spat on the ground in contempt— "I do not have to tell you they fear us like the sharp fang of the rattlesnake."

He went on to boast of their feats and skill in battle, and how they would kill great numbers of the enemy and take many scalps. When he had finished, the Indian braves stood waiting for Colonel Williams' order to march.

Suddenly Ohrante asked, "What do you suppose a battle is like, Thayendanegea?" There was an apprehensive look in his black eyes. Although he was two years older, it was his first time on the warpath too. "What will happen? What will we do when we meet the French?"

Joseph Brant did not reply at once but when he spoke his voice had a confident ring. "It will be exciting," he said, "and our hearts will beat very fast with joy. We will do as Teoniahi-garawe has said, and kill as many of the French and our ancient enemies the Algonquins as we can. Then we'll scalp them, Ohrante. Think of it—coming back to the camp with strings of scalps at our belts!"

Although Ohrante would not admit it to his friend, he was afraid and he hated himself for it. But Joseph Brant's words made him feel better. At the mention of scalps his hand crept to the knife at his belt.

When the order to march was given, old King Hendrick, mounted on a horse, led the Indians in a column out of the camp. Colonel Williams and his white troops followed.

As they silently threaded the rough, deeply rutted road that was little more than a forest path, Ohrante cast a sidelong glance at his companion. What a handsome young brave he was, tall and erect, his dark eyes aglow! There was something about Joseph Brant that was different from other Indians. Was it because of his skin? The Onondaga boy wondered, looking down at his own coppery arms and chest. It was odd about Joseph's light color. . . .

Ohrante had wondered about it ever since he had first met the Mohawk boy while the Indians were camped outside Albany awaiting the arrival of the New England regiments. They were both members of the Wolf Clan, which made them tribal brothers, and they had soon become great friends. One day Joseph had spoken of his birth in the region of the Ohio River, where the Indians' hunting grounds were located, but he had been vague about his father. The settlers often gave the red men names that were easier to pronounce than their Indian ones, and Joseph had taken his stepfather Carrihogo's English name of Brant. Another Mohawk warrior had told Ohrante that Joseph's real father was said to have been an English nobleman. . . .

Looking at his friend, Ohrante felt a twinge of envy. Joseph Brant wasn't afraid . . . If the young Onondaga could have read the Mohawk boy's mind, he might have felt better, for although Joseph took pains to conceal his feelings he, too, was afraid.

Up at the head of the column he could see King Hendrick's restless eyes searching the forest, and he tried to follow their gaze. Had the war chief seen something? Suddenly, off to the left, a partridge flew up with a whir of wings. Joseph Brant jumped as if a gun had gone off, then felt foolish and hoped Ohrante hadn't noticed his alarm.

He kept telling himself that he must not be afraid, that he must justify General Johnson's faith in him. . . .

When the war council was held at Mount Johnson his sister Molly had promised to help him. "You are very young, Thayendanegea," she had said dubiously, "but I will speak to Warraghiyagey of your wish to take the warpath."

Twelve hundred Indians had come to the council. The prows of an armada of elm-bark canoes and dugouts cleft the placid surface of the Mohawk River as the people of Ganegahaga and those from Iconderoga, the Lower Castle of the Mohawks, set out for Mount Johnson. Others journeyed afoot over forest trails through what is today the state and was then the province of New York. There were the Mohawks' neighbors just to the west, the Oneidas; the Onondagas from the center of the lands known as the Long-House of the Six Nations that extended across New York. From farther west came the Cayugas and the powerful Senecas; from a little to the south the Tuscaroras.

For three days the warriors had squatted in the big meadow by the river listening to the long speeches of their chiefs. Then General Johnson had made his war speech. He told the warriors of a French army that was gathering in the north, preparing to sweep down on the English settlements. If it were not stopped it would drive the Six Nations as well as the settlers into the sea.

"Brothers!" Johnson had shouted. "Stand by your true friends, the English! If you desire to treat me as a brother, go with me! My canoe is ready to put into the water, my guns are loaded, my sword is at my side, and my ax is sharpened!"

Then he had raised a great war belt of wampum high over his head and hurled it to the ground. An Oneida chief had darted forward, snatched it up, and held it aloft.

With war whoops and tom-toms dinning in his ears and desperation in his heart, Joseph had watched the war dance begin. Perhaps he would not be able to join the battle against the French. Had Warraghiyagey forgotten him? But at last the general had summoned him. Johnson's handsome face had been graver than Joseph had ever seen it.

"You must forgive me, my brother, that I have not been able to talk to you sooner," he had said. "I did not forget what your sister told me of your wish to take the warpath." Pausing a moment, he had gazed out over the meadow at the dancing warriors, and his dark eyes had become stern. "Weaklings in

an army on the march are like deadfall across the trail. I can
take no risks with them. Every warrior must keep up with the
rest."

"I can keep up, Warraghiyagey!" Joseph had insisted.

"There can be no turning back once a battle is joined. It is
no place for boys. A Mohawk warrior must be a man."

"Because I am a boy in years does not mean I am not a man
in strength and courage, Warraghiyagey! Look at me and you
will see that I am ready to be a warrior!"

General Johnson had nodded. "I see that you have grown in
strength and stature since I last saw you. I have spoken of this
matter to Teoniahigarawe. He has asked me to decide. Very
well—I have decided, Thayendanegea. You will go. . . ."

That was why he couldn't let General Johnson down now.
He had to be brave. If only his heart would stop hammering at
his ribs . . . He glanced again toward the head of the column.
Was Teoniahigarawe expecting trouble? He saw the old war
chief turn in his saddle and gaze back toward the long line of
provincial soldiers with Colonel Williams at its head.

Beside him, Ohrante said, "Teoniahigarawe looks worried."

Joseph tried to keep his voice calm. "He is wondering why
the white officer doesn't send out scouts. Everyone knows you
need scouts on a march in case of an ambush."

The road, which had passed through a deep swamp at first,
led into a heavily wooded valley with high hills on both sides.
On the left, steep, rocky cliffs rose above a gloomy gorge where
a stream flowed through dense underbrush.

"I hope we'll be out of here soon," Ohrante said nervously.
"I don't like it."

Joseph peered toward the gorge. At that moment the sun,
penetrating a cleft in the rocks, glinted on something. Although
his scalp lock was stiff with grease, he felt it crawl. Instinctively
he moved to warn King Hendrick, but the old man had already
reined up his horse. His keen old eyes bored into the tangled

thicket in the gorge. The Mohawk boy could see them glitter.

Hendrick made a sign with his arm that every warrior understood. They started to melt away with swift stealth, but it was too late. At that moment the whole thicket exploded in a blast of fire and smoke. As Joseph dived for cover a warrior directly ahead of him leaped high in the air with an unearthly yell and fell dead at his feet. Scores of others were already stretched on the ground, some motionless, some writhing in agony. Although the enemy were still invisible, their guns belched flame on every side.

Ahead, Hendrick's horse reared up with a frightful scream and fell dead. Struggling clear of the animal's body, the old chief tried to rise, but just then a shadowy figure slithered toward him. Joseph leaped toward Hendrick, but the Montagnais got there first. The enemy Indian raised his musket in both hands, high above his head. The bright, cold steel of the bayonet gleamed as it drove deep into the old chief's body.

As Joseph hurled himself at the Montagnais, he heard the man grunt, and the musket clattered to the ground. Joseph dropped his own gun, for it was useless in a hand-to-hand fight. Then he closed with the Montagnais and they rolled over and over, each clawing for a grip on the other's throat.

Suddenly the young Mohawk's breath was shut off; he was strangling. He stared into the warrior's face, so close to his own —the flat head, the eyes black and cold as a snake's, the skin glistening with greasy war paint. The nose was blue, the eyebrows and cheeks black, and the rest of the face was bright red.

By sheer luck Joseph's hand brushed against the scalping knife in the Montagnais' belt and he seized it. Using his last ounce of strength, he struck for the hideous eyes. For a moment everything went black; then his enemy's grip relaxed and Joseph was breathing again, gasping, sick to his stomach. Still panting, he scalped the dead Montagnais as expertly as if he had done it a hundred times before.

Quickly he took cover in a clump of underbrush. Crouching there, his gun raised, he could see the enemy all around him as they came out of concealment: French regulars, Canadian militia, Indians, and the French-Canadian bush rangers called *coureurs-de-bois,* as wild and savage as the red men themselves.

It was easy to see now why Hendrick had called the French White Jackets in his speech before the march had begun. They were gorgeous in white uniforms aglitter with gold. Joseph stared too at the flag the French color bearer carried—a white banner emblazoned with the golden lilies of France.

The white uniforms made excellent targets against the gloomy green of the forest. One Frenchman, a few yards away, had so much gold on his coat and hat that it seemed certain he was a general.

Joseph leveled his gun at the man, pulled the trigger, and as the musket's recoil thudded into his shoulder he saw the French officer fall. Surprisingly, he felt no emotion: his enemy might have been a stuffed image made by a medicine man to drive out devils.

Back down the road toward the camp, Colonel Williams was trying to rally the column, which had been forced back on its own rear by the murderous fire of the ambush. "Follow me!" he yelled and struck out for a wooded rise of ground to his right. Before he could reach it muskets blazed from the thicket ahead of him and he fell dead.

Now leaderless, Colonel Williams' men began to retreat in wild disorder, trampling those at the rear, who were still being led forward by Lieutenant Colonel Whiting. The French and their Indians were in pursuit, yelling and screeching like demons, shooting down their fleeing enemy.

Joseph wriggled on his stomach toward another bit of cover

back in the forest. As he reached it he saw another figure crouched there, and he breathed easier when he recognized Ohrante. Together they crept back toward the detachment, darting from clump to clump of underbrush, pausing only to reload their guns and fire.

Making a wide circle through the rocky forest, they at last came into a small clearing on an elevation above the road. Both young warriors peered down, their eyes wide.

"Look!" Joseph shouted. "More soldiers! Warraghiyagey has sent more soldiers!"

A reinforcement from General Johnson's camp was coming up the road at a run. Their leader barked a command and they deployed on a wide front and took cover. Gradually the entire force continued to fall back, firing as they went, and their bullets mowed down the pursuing French by scores.

When they came in sight of the camp Joseph Brant realized why General Johnson had been wise in sending only a thousand of the white soldiers to meet the French. The rest of the troops had chopped down great trees in the forest and laid their trunks end to end in front of the camp. This barricade was reinforced with the heavy wagons that had carried the army's equipment from Albany, and the big scows or *bateaux* used on the lake.

Behind it the rest of Johnson's men waited, muskets primed and loaded, ready to give the French a disagreeable surprise. Cannoneers stood by with smoking matches in their hands as the grim cannon muzzles pointed toward the enemy.

While Lieutenant Colonel Whiting's men joined the others behind the barricade, the Indians took cover in the thickets at each end of it. From their concealment Joseph and Ohrante could see the white-coated soldiers and the menacing glitter of their bayonets as they came steadily on. Ahead of them, the French-Canadian militia and Indians were spread out through the woods. All along their line the bloodcurdling war whoop rang out.

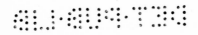

All at once a thunderous explosion shook the ground under Joseph Brant's feet. The cannon along the barricade leaped back in recoil, muzzles belching flame as the grapeshot tore great holes in the advancing French line. Stumbling over the fallen white-clad figures, the rest of the attackers now scurried like ants for the protecting forest.

The battle raged like a storm in which thunder and lightning never stopped. Joseph's part in the fight, like that of his fellow warriors, was one of ceaseless motion. He glided through thickets, picking off the enemy wherever they showed themselves, and the barrel of his musket grew so hot that finally he could no longer touch it. He noted that he had lost track of Ohrante again.

Hearing a great shout, he darted forward to a point where he could see the barricade. The provincial soldiers were leaping over it as, before them, the French and their Indian allies were running for their lives.

Joseph's heart leaped into his throat. The officer leading the white soldiers was not General Johnson but the second-in-command of the army, Colonel Phineas Lyman. What had happened to Warraghiyagey? If the enemy had killed him . . . Hatred surged up in the Mohawk boy's heart and he exulted each time his bullets found their mark.

With yells of triumph the Six Nations warriors joined the provincials in the pursuit, but the enemy scattered into the depths of the forest and were soon lost to view. Gradually all firing ceased and the victorious army made its way back to camp.

Ohrante was already there when Joseph arrived.

"What happened to Warraghiyagey?" Joseph demanded. "Is he all right? Is he—alive?"

"He's all right," his friend replied. "He was wounded slightly in the leg."

His mind relieved, Joseph felt happy and proud that General Johnson's faith in him had not been misplaced. He had been afraid but he had not yielded to it. He had proved himself a warrior.

All around him tired men threw themselves to the ground to rest; others were still bringing in the wounded. Several soldiers came in carrying a wounded man in a French uniform, bright with gold. Blood had soaked his white breeches on one leg and around his hip. An angry murmur went up from some of the older warriors who were nearby. "Kill him!" Joseph heard one of them cry out. "The devils of White Jackets have slain our great leader, King Hendrick. Kill the Frenchman!"

Several Indians started toward the wounded officer, their tomahawks raised, but a provincial officer stepped in with a threatening gesture and they fell back.

"Carry him to the general's tent," he ordered and the older warriors followed as the soldiers bore him away.

Agog with curiosity but not daring to go inside the tent, the two young braves scuttled around to the side. Lying flat on the ground, they pulled up the canvas and peered inside but they could see only the legs of the warriors. They wriggled farther back and tried again. Now they could see better.

Propped up by pillows, General Johnson was half reclining on a cot. Two surgeons were working over the flesh wound in his thigh.

The provincial officer saluted. "This is Baron Dieskau, the enemy commander, who has been wounded, General."

The general motioned to the soldiers to put the French commander on his bed. "Your servant, Baron Dieskau," he said. "It is a pleasure to welcome so brave a man to my camp. I regret that we must meet under circumstances so unfavorable to yourself, sir, but these are the fortunes of war."

He turned to the two surgeons. "Attend to Baron Dieskau's wounds at once, gentlemen. My own is slight and can wait."

"Give the White Jacket to us, Warraghiyagey," one of the

warriors demanded. "King Hendrick has been slain and the French devil must die."

"No, brother," replied General Johnson firmly. "The Frenchman is my prisoner and I shall do with him as I think best. You have already had your revenge for Hendrick's death and you will have many scalps to prove it."

A long and bitter argument in the Indian tongue followed. The braves' faces were sullen, and at last one motioned to the rest and without a word they filed out of the tent. The two boys watched the warriors curiously. Anger smoldered in their eyes.

In spite of his affection for General Johnson, Joseph was puzzled. Among his people a captive received no mercy. He was either tomahawked and scalped immediately or put to fiendish torture. To an Indian, who knew no other rule of warfare, this seemed just.

The warriors huddled together, talking in tones too low to be heard. At length they turned and went back inside the tent. Joseph and Ohrante peered in again.

The braves no longer looked sullen as one by one they came forward and gave Dieskau their hands in friendship. The two boys exchanged questioning glances. What had the warriors discussed outside the tent? Had they really accepted Johnson's demand that the prisoner be spared?

Since the excitement seemed to be over, Joseph and Ohrante started for the Indians' part of the camp. Groups of warriors were coming in from the battleground and the surrounding forest, strings of bloody scalps dangling from their belts. Around their necks, some of the returning braves had silver medallions, or gorgets, worn by officers; one was wearing a gold-laced, three-cornered hat; another proudly held up a bloody finger with a gold ring still on it.

Joseph thought again of how Baron Dieskau had been saved

from death or torture. Perhaps, after all, the way of the white men in sparing a fallen foe was the right one. But had the warriors who had sought to kill Dieskau been convinced of it?

He found an answer to the question the next morning when he heard a commotion and wild yells coming from a nearby tent. As he ran toward it two figures, locked together, came flying out of the tent. One was a provincial colonel; the other was one of the warriors who had demanded Dieskau be turned over to them.

Suddenly the colonel shook himself clear of the Indian and struck a swinging blow that knocked the savage to the ground.

"Get out of here, you red son of Lucifer!" the officer shouted. "If you come around here again, I'll kill you as I would a mad dog!"

The Indian got slowly to his feet, and Joseph saw that he had a knife in his hand. He took a step toward the officer, his black eyes blazing hatred, but as the white man brandished his sword the warrior turned and fled. As he ran he bumped square into Joseph.

He made a threatening gesture with his weapon but lowered it when he saw he had run into one of his own people.

"What happened?" the Mohawk boy cried.

"I went to kill the French devil that Warraghiyagey refused to give us," the warrior grunted. "He is in the tent there, guarded by the dog of a white officer." Still mumbling threats, he went off toward his own tent, and Joseph wandered down to the shore. He wanted to be alone, where he could think more clearly.

Beyond Lake George, he knew, the lake called Champlain reached far to the north. There were no white men's roads in the wilderness surrounding it, but Lake Champlain itself was a watery path to Canada. Could General Johnson's army now advance up it, take Crown Point, sweep on to Montreal and Quebec, and drive the French from North America?

Joseph found his thoughts turning once again to the warriors' rage against his hero, General Johnson, and their treachery in trying to kill Baron Dieskau. Somehow, he knew, he was different. He could understand the white men's mercy.

Chapter 2

Long ripples formed a spreading V as the bow of the elmbark canoe cleft the still surface of the Mohawk River, dark green with the reflection of the forest wall that crowded the very edge of the stream on both sides. Ever since leaving the Upper Castle of the Mohawks that morning, the canoe, driven by the powerful strokes of Joseph Brant's paddle, had made its way downstream. Now, in mid-afternoon of this fine spring day in 1756, nearly a year after the victory at Lake George, it rounded a bend and swung in toward shore.

Here a large cleared expanse of meadowland stretched back from the river bank toward a great stone mansion. Joseph had often seen Mount Johnson, but its elegance never failed to impress him. Now once more he gazed in awe at the massive three-story structure, its tall brick chimneys and its many windows with their panes of real glass.

The canoe's speed slackened and its keel grated gently on the pebbles of the shore. Leaping out first, the young warrior assisted his mother to land. His stepfather Carrihogo followed and, going ahead, led his family in Indian file up the path toward the mansion.

The black servant in gorgeous livery who came to the door recognized the Brant family and ushered them into a great reception hall that was paneled in dark polished wood and hung with tapestries depicting hunting scenes in England.

"I will tell Lady Johnson and Sir William that you are here," he said.

Joseph stared in astonishment. Although his parents spoke no English, he had learned enough of it while he was with the army at Lake George to know that the titles the servant had mentioned were used only for nobility. Lady Johnson? Sir William? What did it mean?

While they waited, Joseph stole a glance at his mother, who was sitting on the edge of her chair, her moonlike face abashed by all the magnificence about her. She was not old but the young warrior noticed how work-worn her hands were. He wished he could build a house like this for her, so that she would not have to toil in the fields and could have servants to wait on her.

A few moments later Molly rushed in, greeting them affectionately, talking very fast, and asking questions in the Mohawk language.

Joseph gazed proudly at his pretty, vivacious sister. In contrast to most Indian girls, she was tall, straight, and slim; and like her younger brother she had a complexion that was light for an Indian's. Her gown of rich silk and the way in which her lustrous black hair was done were both in the fashion of the white women.

In answer to their questions she told them, "The King, the great English father of the Hodenosaunee, has made Warraghiyagey an English sachem for his victory over the French at Lake George. He has the title of baronet and is called Sir William Johnson."

"And you—you are Lady Johnson!" Joseph exclaimed.

"Yes, Thayendanegea. And the council of the people in England called the Parliament has sent Warraghiyagey a gift of five thousand pounds. That is a great deal of money, my brother— more than all the beaver the hunters of the Hodenosaunee can trap in one season are worth."

She left her younger brother marveling as she turned to their mother, for she had many questions to ask, about the family, about her older brothers and their families, and about the friends she had known in Ganegahaga in her girlhood days.

Sir William Johnson came in, greeted them cordially, and after he and Carrihogo had lighted their pipes they all fell to talking together in the Mohawk language.

Joseph had last seen the baronet in all the magnificence of a general's scarlet, white, and gold uniform. Today he made just as commanding a figure in a suit of crimson broadcloth and a white satin waistcoat. The King in England had made no mistake in giving him the title of a noble, the Mohawk boy thought.

Sir William had not followed up his victory at Lake George, for he had decided he would need reinforcements in order to strike at the eight thousand troops of the main French Army at Crown Point. By the time he could get them winter would be approaching. But now he said nothing of plans for striking at the French again. In spite of all his good fortune he seemed to have a careworn look, and Joseph wondered what had caused it.

After a time the baronet and the young Mohawk drew a little apart from the others, talking of the days they had spent on the warpath the summer before.

"It is good to see you again, Thayendanegea," Sir William said. "This is the first chance I have had to tell you that I am proud of you, my brother. You have justified the confidence I had in you when I agreed to let you go with the army. The chiefs spoke highly of your courage in the battle at Lake George. Even though you were only thirteen years old, you proved yourself a true Mohawk warrior."

While the young brave glowed with pleasure, the baronet got up, went to the fireplace, and knocked the ashes from his pipe. When he sat down again he continued, "I have great hopes for you, my brother. Perhaps you will be a great leader of your people. I cannot say yet. It is not given to all men to be leaders."

Joseph Brant's eyes were fixed on Sir William's face. In the baronet's handsome, dark features he saw not only the kindliness and understanding that had made him beloved of the Indians but the resolution that had enabled him to become a general and now a nobleman, honored by the King.

Joseph said earnestly, "How will I know whether I am a leader, Warraghiyagey?"

"Sooner or later you will be tested. If you meet the test when it comes, you will know . . ."

The young Mohawk's forehead was furrowed. "A test?" he repeated. "What kind of a test, Warraghiyagey?"

"I do not know," said Sir William. "I cannot tell you when or where it will come, but it will."

Joseph was thoughtful for a moment. Then he said eagerly, "If I could become a leader perhaps, when the war is over, I could . . . do things for my people." He gazed about the comfortably furnished room. "I would like to help them learn better ways of living . . ."

"You are young to have such thoughts, Thayendanegea," said the baronet. "I am glad you realize how much your people need help."

He refilled his pipe and then went on. "Even if you prove yourself a leader it will not be enough. King Hendrick was a leader, but he did not lead his people to better ways of living. Neither has his brother Little Abraham, who became war chief of the Hodenosaunee after Hendrick's death. The man who does that must have more than leadership and might in battle."

He rose and turned to the others in the room. "There are some matters of business that I must attend to," he said. "If you will excuse me for a time I will join you later at dinner."

Joseph saw a worried look cross his sister's face as Sir William left the room. When he had gone she said, "Warraghiyagey is having trouble with the Bostonian sachem, Governor William Shirley of Massachusetts, who has been appointed a general to command the King's armies in America. As you know, Warraghiyagey is the King's superintendent of Indian affairs. General Shirley has interfered and appointed his own agents to deal with the Indians."

"We have heard of that at Ganegahaga," said Carrihogo. "The sachem Shirley's agents are friendly with the Dutch traders in Albany, who so often cheated and abused us until Warraghiyagey put a stop to it. I have heard that they are ill-treating some of our people again. Why doesn't Shirley realize that Warraghiyagey is the only white man we can trust to treat us fairly?"

Molly shook her head sadly and said, "I am afraid, Thayendanegea, that it may be a long time before you will take the warpath again with Warraghiyagey. The Bostonian sachem is jealous of him because of his success against the French and the title the King has given him."

Although Joseph had never heard of Governor William Shirley until now, a fierce hatred stirred in his breast for this man who had caused his hero so much trouble. How long would it be before Sir William led another army against the French? And how long before his own test of leadership would come?

After the war had continued for some time without a decisive advantage for either side, William Shirley was relieved of his command of the King's armies, raising Joseph's hopes that he might soon return to the warpath. Meanwhile, however, many of the warriors of the Six Nations, tired of inaction, had been coaxed by the French to turn against the British. Sir William accepted the difficult task of winning them back to the English side.

Reconciled to the delay, the young warrior waited, trying to be patient. He hunted, fished, and roamed the forest trails. A year went by . . . two . . . Then it was winter again and snow lay deep over the wilderness as the great New Year's Jubilee of the Mohawks began early in February, 1759. Joseph was now nearly seventeen.

When he woke on the morning of the Jubilee's fifth day his mother and stepfather were already up. Shivering in the cold of the sleeping chamber, he hurriedly dressed, threw his blanket over his shoulders, and went into the central part of the section occupied by the Brant family in the long house.

It was warmer there. Joseph's mother was filling a stone bowl with sagamite from the large brass kettle that hung steaming over the fire. She went up to her husband Carrihogo, who was squatting on the ground, and handed him the bowl and crude stone spoon.

Joseph stood before the fire to warm himself. "Why didn't you call me?" he asked his mother. "You know I wanted to be up early for the Sacrifice of the White Dog."

His mother gazed at him, her black eyes a little puzzled. "But there is plenty of time, Thayendanegea," she replied. "I wanted to give your stepfather his breakfast first. He has to meet with the other Keepers of the Faith in the council chamber before the procession starts, you know."

"Why are you always so impatient, Thayendanegea?" Carrihogo asked. "One would think you were an old man with only a few moons left to him instead of a young warrior who has many years ahead. Aren't the days long enough for you?"

In the warmth of the fire Joseph stretched his limbs lazily and squatted beside his stepfather.

"There are so many things to be done," he said. "I do not like to let any time go to waste."

"Things?" Carrihogo repeated. "What things that a boy can do are so important? Games? Ball? Wrestling? Leaping and running races? Besides, you cannot do those things in the winter anyway."

The Mohawk boy's mother handed him a bowl of sagamite. He ate a mouthful before he replied. The thin, hot mush of pounded corn flavored with dried fish tasted good on this bitter morning.

"No, Carrihogo," he said, "I was not thinking of games."

"Then is it because you are impatient to take the warpath again with Warraghiyagey?"

Joseph edged a little closer to the fire. In spite of its warmth he could feel a draft on his shoulder. The long house, built of a double row of tall saplings set close together in the ground, then bent over, lashed together to form the roof, and covered with elm bark, was not tight enough to keep out the wintry blasts. He peered up over his head where the firelight flickered on strings of corn and squashes hung to dry. Above them, where the smoke went out through a hole in the arched roof, he could hear the wind whistling.

It was true that he was impatient to take the warpath again. Yet it was not of war alone that he had been thinking. If he spoke what was in his mind, he wondered, would his stepfather understand? Well, there was no time for it anyway. Carrihogo had spooned up the last of his sagamite and now rose and went through the central passage of the long house toward the council chamber in the middle of the structure that stretched for a hundred feet within the stockade of Ganegahaga.

When he had gone, Joseph hurried to finish his own breakfast. Already the muffled beat of tom-toms could be heard. As he stood up his mother's eyes fell proudly on him.

"You look very handsome in your new things, Thayendanegea," she said.

Joseph's face glowed with pleasure at the words. "I am grateful to you, my mother, for making them," he said.

She had set to work on the clothes as soon as it had become known that he had been selected as one of the band to perform the Feather Dance, which was one of the main features at the Sacrifice of the White Dog. The soft deerskin of the short-skirted kilt, leggings, tunic, and moccasins was bright with the intricate colored designs she had embroidered with such care in beads and porcupine quills. Around his neck hung a leather neckpiece with the symbol of the Wolf Clan on it; and from the crown of the *gustoweh,* or headdress, slanted the single eagle feather of the Mohawk warrior.

"The glances of all the maidens will be upon you today, Thayendanegea," his mother said. She spoke a little regretfully, as if she realized that he would soon be grown up and ready for marriage.

"Why should I care for maidens' glances when I have you to love and look after me, my mother?" Joseph replied, but he could not conceal a gleam in his eye.

His mother looked pleased. She was very proud of him. With her daughter Molly married to General Johnson and away from home, and her other sons also married with homes of their own, the thought that her youngest son was in no hurry to leave her was a happy one.

"I must go now and join the rest who will take part in the Feather Dance," the young brave said, "but I will see you at the ceremony in the council chamber."

He started down the central passageway of the long house. It led through the rooms where other families had their cooking fires and past the sleeping chambers on both sides of the passage. Everyone was hurrying, finishing breakfast, and pressing toward the door at the end.

Outside, the frigid breath of the early morning made Joseph gasp. Alongside him a laughing voice said, "Surely it is not too cold for the mighty warrior Thayendanegea!"

It was Owathaka, daughter of Chief Tahkarihoken; her English name was Catherine. For a moment Joseph's pride was offended by her laughter, but the gaiety and good nature in Catherine's eyes were infectious and he laughed too.

"It feels like a knife thrust into my chest," he admitted. "On such a day as this perhaps it is better to stay by the fire in the long house."

"Oh, but it is such a beautiful morning, Thayendanegea! Just look at that sky!"

He halted beside her, his eyes following her pointing finger. The sun had not yet thrust its head above the three rows of high wooden palisades that encircled the village; but the sky in the east was aflame with red and gold above the bare gray branches of oaks and maples and the green of pine and spruce in the wall of forest beyond the stockade.

The young Mohawk's eyes shifted back to the village. A white blanket of snow covered the ground and the roofs of the long houses, from whose doors streams of warriors, squaws, and children were pouring. In the center of the village stood a tall pole, forked at the top. From one of the prongs hung the White Dog. On the first day of the New Year's Jubilee it had been killed, great care having been used to shed no blood nor to break any of its bones. Now, with its white fur covered with dots of red paint, ornamented with feathers, a string of white wampum about its neck, it dangled, frozen stiff, swaying a little in the wind.

"We had better join the other feather dancers, Thayendanegea," Catherine said. "The procession is forming near the wall of the stockade."

As they started toward the stockade Joseph marveled at
Catherine's lightness. His own moccasined feet broke through
the crust of the snow but she glided over it like some airborne
sprite, laughing as he floundered. No wonder, even though
she was only thirteen, she had been chosen to take part in the
Feather Dance, he reflected. She was certainly a pretty little
thing in a costume much like his own, save that her skirt was
longer than his kilt and she wore a neckpiece of the Turtle
Clan. He noticed the dark gloss of her hair, parted in the middle
with two long braids flying out behind and, as she turned back
to look at him, the radiant coppery glow of her face.

She was waiting for him, smiling, when he came up with
rest of the feather dancers. Just ahead he could see his stepfather
among the Keepers of the Faith, honored men and women selected from among the older warriors and matrons, and including all the chiefs. Behind the dancers the rest of the people
were assembling in a long straggling line.

Carrihogo, selected to officiate at the ceremony, held up his
hand and gave a command. The tom-toms began to beat again
and the procession moved off with a slow, dignified step toward
the White Dog. It circled the pole and halted. Carrihogo ordered the dog cut down. Four other Keepers placed it on a litter
made of bark. Then the procession moved on again.

The long house where the Brant family lived was the one in
which the central council chamber was located. Just outside it
a platform of logs had been put up. On this rude altar a fire
was laid ready for kindling.

The procession began to circle slowly around it. Then Carrihogo gave a signal and the four bearers laid the White Dog
on a bench before the altar. Another of the Keepers of the
Faith glided into the long house, came out carrying a flaming
brand from one of the cooking fires, and thrust it into the
pile of firewood.

To the slow beat of the tom-toms the procession continued

until it had surrounded the altar in a wide circle. As the drums stopped beating and it halted, the four bearers lifted the White Dog, advanced to the altar, facing the rising sun, and laid the sacrifice on the flames.

Carrihogo, standing before the altar, raised his arm. Three times he shouted a hail: "Qua! qua! qua!"

The people responded with a deep-throated "Ho! ho!"

Then Carrihogo began the prayer of thanksgiving to the Great Spirit. Raising his arms, he intoned: "Hawenneyu! Listen to our words! We have assembled for our celebration of Giyewanousquagowa, the New Year's Jubilee, as thou commanded our ancestors to do. By this ancient custom we have sacrificed the White Dog."

Here Carrihogo paused and cast dried leaves of Indian tobacco on the fire.

"Hawenneyu!" he went on as clouds of blue smoke rose from the altar. "Continue to listen! The soul of the White Dog, ascending to heaven, returns our thanks that thou hast preserved so many of us for another year. It is also our pledge of fidelity to thee."

Carrihogo went on and on, giving thanks for each of the blessings the people had enjoyed. Standing beside Catherine, Joseph shivered.

"I wish my stepfather would get finished," he whispered. "He is so near the fire, perhaps he doesn't realize how bitter the wind is."

Catherine smiled. "It has been the custom to make long speeches since ancient days, you know, Thayendanegea," she whispered back, "and I suppose it always will be."

The Mohawk boy sighed. "Sometimes I think it would be better, Owathaka, if our people talked less and did more to make their lives better and more comfortable."

But at last, when the White Dog was consumed by the flames, Carrihogo ended his speech. As the drums beat again, the people filed into the council chamber and formed another circle, squatting on the floor about the fire, which had already been lighted. Two warriors with turtle-shell rattles took their places on a bench in the center.

"You will be warm enough when the Feather Dance starts, Thayendanegea," Catherine said. "See! The singers are beginning their songs. We had better take our places."

Joseph slipped off his tunic and laid it on the ground. Like the other warriors among the feather dancers he stood bare to the waist except for bracelets of beads and shells about his arms, his Wolf Clan neckpiece, and a necklace of bear's claws.

The two warriors in the center were finishing their song, beating a slow cadence with their rattles. As they began another the beat quickened. Behind Catherine, Joseph swung easily into the rhythm of the Feather Dance.

The dance lasted nearly half an hour. When it was over, both Catherine and Joseph were breathing hard and the young warrior's bare arms, chest, and back glistened with perspiration. They squatted among the spectators to watch other dances that followed.

"I like the Feather Dance best," Catherine remarked.

"It is graceful," Joseph replied, "but it does not make the heart beat fast like the war dance."

The daughter of Chief Tahkarihoken looked up at him. "Because you are a warrior, do you think of nothing but war?"

Joseph's face became serious. "No, Owathaka, I think of many other things besides war."

As he spoke the squaws entered the council chamber bearing steaming kettles of succotash made of the corn, beans, and squash that were the Mohawks' principal food. Behind them came half a dozen others struggling under the burden of a huge iron pot.

Catherine sniffed. "That smells like meat," she said.

"It is," Joseph replied. "Didn't you hear how lucky the hunting party was that went out before the celebration began? They came across a herd of deer stranded in a hollow by deep drifts."

Watching the squaws who were carrying the heavy pot of venison stew, Joseph saw one stagger and almost fall. It was his mother. It came to him that she was still doing work that was now too much for her: cooking all the meals, making clothes for her husband and son, toiling long hours in the fields under the blazing summer sun.

Noticing his silence, Catherine asked, "What are you thinking of, Thayendanegea?"

He was wondering if the slim, pretty little Indian girl beside him would also become toil-worn in a few years, losing her beauty early, as most squaws did. But he replied, "I told you I did not always think of war, Owathaka. I have been wondering why our people cannot learn to do some things the way the white settlers do."

"What do you mean?"

Before answering, Joseph pointed toward the kettles of succotash and venison stew. A line of warriors was already forming and the squaws were ladling the food into bowls.

"Do you know what will happen at the feast?" he said. "The food will be eaten until the kettles are empty and the marrow sucked from the last venison bone. The white settlers do not do that."

"But this is a time for rejoicing and feasting," Catherine said.

"More food is always prepared than is needed. Most of the warriors gorge themselves until they are sick. Yet each year there is never enough food to last until our new crops are ripe, and for many weeks the people do not have enough to eat."

He paused a moment, frowning. "Why?" he cried. "It is not that way with the white settlers. They raise enough to last them. Why, Owathaka?"

"I do not know." Catherine was looking down, twisting a

bracelet on her wrist. Then she glanced up at him shyly from under her dark lashes. "You are . . . different, Thayenda-negea," she said softly. "Other warriors of our Nation do not think of these things, but you do."

"I think of them—but thinking is not enough!" the young Mohawk said fiercely. "I want to find a way for our people to have more food, better houses, and better clothes, as the white men do."

"You will find the way someday, Thayendanegea," Catherine said. "I am sure you will."

Her confidence made him even more determined. Then he smiled at her. "Just because some of the people eat more than is good for them at a feast is no reason we should eat nothing," he said. "I'm hungry, Owathaka. Let us go and get some of that succotash and venison stew." He helped Catherine to her feet and they went to join the crowd around the kettles.

Two more days of ceremonies, speechmaking, dancing, and feasting followed the Sacrifice of the White Dog. When Joseph got up on the morning after the Jubilee ended, he could hear the wind's howl as it battered at the long house. It was bitter cold in the drafty sleeping chamber.

His stepfather was still sleeping off the effects of the final feast. Joseph's teeth chattered as he hustled into his clothes and went into the central room, where his mother was busy preparing breakfast. He crept close to the fire while she ladled out a bowl of sagamite.

When she handed it to him he looked first into the bowl and then inquiringly at her. "You have only filled it half full," he said. "Did you think I would not be hungry after the feast?"

His mother shook her head. "It is not that. You are always hungry, I know, Thayendanegea. But so much of our store of food was used for the feasts that we will have to be careful of what is left." Noticing his frown, she added hopefully, "There

are only two more moons before spring. Then there will be
fish to add to what we have, and perhaps game."

Something cold lit on the tip of Joseph's nose and melted. He
looked up at the hole in the roof above the fire. Through it he
could see snow swirling in the gray light of the morning.

"When I have eaten I will go down to the river," he said,
raising his voice to make himself heard over the blast of the wind
that shook the walls and sent chill gusts through its loose bark
covering. "I have some lines set there through the ice. Perhaps
there will be fish on some of them."

Quickly he finished the bowl of sagamite and started for the
end of the long house that lay nearest the river. As he passed
through the council chamber he saw many evidences of last
night's feast. The floor was littered with bones and pieces of
hide that had remained clinging to the venison when it was put
into the stew. Empty kettles stood about, and in one corner
three warriors snored loudly where, stuffed with food, they had
flung themselves down in a stupor. Joseph's nose wrinkled in
distaste at the lingering smell of grease and stale food.

Farther along, other families were having their breakfasts;
here, too, the smell of grease was oppressive. The wind, sweeping over the roof, forced the smoke of the cooking fires back
into the long house, and the stench made Joseph cough. He observed that many of the people, their faces pinched by the cold,
sat huddled under ragged, filthy, and grease-stained blankets.

In one chamber a man lay coughing, but Joseph knew by the
sound it was not because of the smoke. The warrior, close to the
fire, was being racked by a terrible spasm. One of his arms lay
outside the blanket, and the Mohawk boy saw that it was little
more than skin and bone. Why, he wondered, did the cough
that made people waste away and die strike so many more Indians than white men?

As he pushed through the door at the end of the long house
a great blast of wind seized him as if with the powerful hand

of a giant and drove him back inside. He fought his way out again, into a silent, blinding white world, buffeted by the driving blizzard. He strained his eyes, trying to pierce the swirling storm, but he could see nothing but the drifts being piled up against the long house. He could not even detect the outlines of the stockade, only a few yards away.

To flounder out into the storm would be foolhardy: even if he could find the stockade gate, he would be swallowed up beyond it before he reached the river, perhaps unable to find his way back again.

Fiercely Joseph raised his fist toward the sky and shook it, but it was not just the storm at which his anger was directed. He made a solemn vow to himself:

"I will find a way to end the miseries of my people!"

Chapter 3

At last, when summer came, Joseph Brant took the warpath once more. So successful had Sir William Johnson been in winning back the Six Nations warriors that, although a few remained with the French, he was able to muster a force of nine hundred braves.

Three English armies moved to strike at the enemy on every front. General James Wolfe, with a mighty army supported by a fleet of warships, sailed up the Saint Lawrence River to attack

Quebec. General Jeffery Amherst advanced toward the French forts at Ticonderoga and Crown Point with orders to take them, march into Canada, and meet Wolfe at Quebec.

The third army, of two thousand white soldiers under General John Prideaux, moved from Oswego on Lake Ontario against the enemy stronghold of Fort Niagara. With them went Sir William and his nine hundred warriors. There at Oswego, Joseph and his Onondaga friend Ohrante met once more in joyful reunion, eager for new adventures on the warpath.

Smoke from the breakfast fires of the army besieging Fort Niagara curled up lazily into the hot sky of the July morning. Sitting before theirs after finishing their meal, Joseph and Ohrante lit their pipes and sat looking toward where the Niagara River flowed into Lake Ontario.

Out there tongues of orange flame licked up continually from the hidden muzzles of the cannon and mortars in the trenches that the British engineers, tunneling like moles, had extended toward the fort. As another of the thunderous explosions shook the earth the two braves saw flames shoot high in the air from within the ramparts of the French stronghold on the peninsula that jutted out between the river and the lake.

"There's another one!" Joseph cried. "Those must be wooden barracks and storehouses that the red-hot balls from Warraghiyagey's guns are setting afire inside the fort."

"The balls must be killing many of the White Jackets too," Ohrante replied. "And the French cannon fire is not as heavy as it was. How much longer can they hold out? Warraghiyagey's guns have been firing for three suns now, night and day, and——"

The rest of his words were drowned out as three of the British cannon went off almost at the same moment. Ohrante, watching, leaped to his feet.

"Look there, Thayendanegea!" he shouted. "Do you see

what has happened? The guns have blown a big hole in the walls of the fort."

Joseph also stood up and craned his neck in the direction of the fort, where the white ensign of France, with its golden lilies, still floated defiantly.

"They'll have to surrender now," he said. "I hear the French have only six hundred soldiers. With so many of the enemy's cannon knocked out, Warraghiyagey's Red Jackets can advance through the hole in the walls and kill every White Jacket in the fort."

Ohrante's look was dejected. "Yes," he said, "and we will see none of our kind of fighting. We might just as well have stayed in the Long House of the Hodenosaunee."

With no French scalps at their belts, the Indians were restless. If the enemy soldiers did not come out and fight and the fort surrendered, Joseph was afraid his fellow warriors would desert. General Prideaux had been killed when a mortar burst at the start of the bombardment, and Sir William had taken command of the entire army. He would very much need his Indians for the wilderness warfare when he moved toward the French posts in the west or down the Saint Lawrence River toward Montreal. And now even Ohrante, who had remained loyal to Sir William when most of the Onondagas had gone over to the French, was dissatisfied.

Fort Niagara, which had resisted desperately in hopes that troops from one of the French posts to the west would come to the rescue, surely could not hold out much longer. Only a day or so before, Joseph and Ohrante had gone out with a scouting party to look for the enemy reinforcement. They had searched a long way up the river, and for the first time in their lives the two young braves had gazed spellbound at the mighty, curving horseshoe of raging waters, with its mist-cloud above and its greenish boiling turbulence below that was the falls of Niagara. But there had been no trace of the enemy.

As Joseph stood mulling over these discouraging thoughts, a trumpet blast in the camp brought him out of his reverie.

"I wonder what that means," said Ohrante.

"Something must have happened," the Mohawk brave replied. "See! the Red Jackets are hurrying toward the parade ground. We had better go too."

The scarlet-clad regiments were forming their ranks when the two warriors reached the parade. The Indians were also coming in and were gathered at one end of the area with Little Abraham, their war chief, at their head.

Sir William Johnson and his staff came up and stood before the army. The commander ordered his officers to come forward.

"A scout has brought word that a French detachment is coming down the river to reinforce the fort's garrison," he told them. "Our men who are now in the trenches will remain there to repel any attack from the fort. Of the rest, half will guard our boats, which must not be destroyed. Captain De Lancey, you will take a hundred and fifty of the light infantry and all of the Indians up the river. You are to prevent the enemy from reaching the fort."

The Indians, ahead of Captain De Lancey's men, started out treading softly along the forest trail. A mile up the river Captain De Lancey ordered a halt. While the Indians watched, scornful of men who did squaws' work, the British soldiers plied picks and shovels, throwing up a breastwork with one of its ends on the river bank. That night, while the detachment lay with its arms close at hand and no fires to light the darkness, De Lancey sent out a small reconnoitering party. It never returned. About dawn a volley of gunfire told of its fate and the approach of the enemy.

The British captain sent a courier back to the camp for reinforcements. Lieutenant Colonel Eyre Massey came up with a hundred and fifty men and took over command.

Massey placed his main force back of the breastwork. "The

light infantry and the Indians will take cover to the left to shield our unprotected flank," he ordered.

The Indians dissolved into the forest. Side by side, Joseph and Ohrante crept forward to take a position a little ahead of the light infantry. They stopped every few feet to listen, but the silence of the woods was broken only by the songs of the birds and the occasional bark of a squirrel. The other Indians seemed to have vanished, though the two warriors knew they were close by.

Suddenly Joseph touched Ohrante's arm. Both Indians froze like stone images. Stealing toward them, his bronzed body almost invisible against the brown carpet of dead leaves on the ground, was a strange Indian.

Instantly the Mohawk warrior raised his musket and fired, but Ohrante with a lightning-like movement struck the gun to one side. The ball went wide. At the sound of the explosion the strange Indian held up his hand.

"Don't fire again, Thayendanegea!" Ohrante warned. "He is an Onondaga. He is asking for a council."

The two glided toward the Onondaga. As if by magic other Indians appeared. Some Joseph recognized as Sir William's warriors; others he knew must be Onondagas who had remained with the French.

The Indian at whom Joseph had fired spoke: "Brothers! You are fools to fight against the White Jackets. Unless you join us you and your families will be driven into the sea with the English. Go and tell your brothers of Warraghiyagey's army that this is so. If they come with us now, it will not be too late. There will be much good fighting and plenty of English scalps for us all."

His words caused some of Sir William's braves to look questioningly at each other.

Then Joseph knew. This was his test . . . The French, striking at Colonel Massey's weakened flank, might gain the victory and relieve the fort's garrison if the loyal warriors deserted now.

Already some of them had moved a few paces toward the renegade Onondagas. Even Ohrante took a hesitant step in their direction. It came to Joseph that only a strong leader could keep them from going over to the French.

He faced his fellow warriors. "This traitor lies, my brothers! It is the French who will be driven into the sea. Warraghiyagey has promised it!"

The disloyal Onondaga grunted scornfully. "Do not be deceived by the promises of Warraghiyagey. Why did he wait so long to take the warpath? Was he afraid of the might of the White Jackets? Did he know that their numbers are as many as the leaves of all the trees in the forest? Come with us, brothers, if you want to live and fight again after today!"

Joseph Brant advanced a step toward his companions. His dark eyes held the proud and fearless look of the eagle.

"Shame!" he cried. "Are you going to desert Warraghiyagey, your true friend? Has he ever broken a promise to you? Has he ever shown treachery toward his brothers of the Hodenosaunee?"

He pointed an accusing finger toward the renegade Onondagas. "No! These are the treacherous ones, these warriors who have broken faith with Warraghiyagey and caused brother to fight brother!"

Joseph turned his gaze upon Ohrante. With a shamefaced look his friend came back and stood beside him.

Then the young Mohawk faced the other warriors who had moved toward the renegades. He held up his hand solemnly. "I, Thayendanegea of the Mohawks, promise you we will win the victory over the White Jackets today. If we do not, I will join the squaws by the fires in the long house and never take the warpath again!"

After hearing his impassioned vow, the warriors who had

been on the point of deserting moved back toward him while the renegades scowled at him blackly. One of them grunted and without a word they all slunk into the forest.

At that moment a war whoop sounded in the distance. Joseph motioned in the direction of the breastwork. The others followed him, falling back slightly toward where the British light infantry lay protecting Colonel Massey's flank.

With Ohrante beside him, Joseph took cover. The two braves lay motionless and silent, waiting.

Off to the right, wild yells echoed through the woodland. The two braves peering out from the underbrush saw the enemy burst out of the forest on the run, hurling themselves straight at the breastwork. Unchallenged, they came on—wild-eyed, half-savage *coureurs-de-bois*, Indians, white-coated French regulars.

As Joseph watched, he wondered what had happened to Colonel Massey's men. Had they retreated?

Then, like a lightning bolt, a blinding flash lit the somber glades of the forest. The breastwork disappeared in a cloud of flame and smoke as the echo of the volley rolled through the wilderness. In what, an instant before, had been a solid enemy line, Joseph saw gaping holes. White-coated officers, yelling and brandishing their swords, were urging their men on, but the line wavered, broke, and fled for cover, leaving its dead and wounded strewn before the breastwork.

In a forest that had suddenly become as silent as if it were deserted, Joseph lay in his concealment beside Ohrante, his muscles as taut as those of a panther crouched to spring, a finger on the trigger of his ready musket, his ear cocked to catch the slightest crackle of a twig.

Again it came without warning—the enemy, rallied by their officers, catapulting out of the shadows in a wide sweep toward the flank. Now it was the Indians and light infantry who met the oncoming wave with a fury like that of hornets in a stirred-up nest.

Joseph's hands were steady on his gun. He fired calmly, reloaded, fired again, and each time he saw his target go down. As he looked down his musket barrel he could see men falling everywhere, yet the enemy swept on. Would they, in spite of all, turn the flank and fall on Colonel Massey's men from the rear?

Suddenly the line crumpled and fell to pieces. Joseph gave a yell of triumph. "Come on!" he shouted to Ohrante. "They're running! After them!"

It was mid-afternoon when they returned, exhausted but happy after chasing the enemy for miles, scalps dangling from their belts.

Joseph clutched Ohrante's arm and pointed ahead. The two friends halted, gazing into the distance at Fort Niagara on its triangle of ground between the river and the lake.

The afternoon sun glinted on the golden lilies of the white ensign of France as it came fluttering down the flagstaff over the ramparts. A moment later another banner climbed slowly up. At the top, while Sir William Johnson's cannon belched a thunderous salute, the Union Jack of England floated out in the breeze. Now the English were masters of the Great Lakes and the lands to the west.

Within him Joseph's heart swelled with pride and gladness. His long-awaited test had come and he had met it squarely. He could lead men, make them do his will!

And his promise of victory had been fulfilled too. Joseph Brant would not have to join the squaws by the fires in the long house.

Chapter 4

The long French and Indian War was over. Soon after Sir William Johnson's conquest of Fort Niagara, General Wolfe took Quebec in the famous battle on the Plains of Abraham in which both he and the French commander, Montcalm, were killed. The following summer Montreal fell. The British were masters of all Canada.

Now that peace had come, Joseph Brant could think of the resolution he had made during the New Year's Jubilee. How was he to go about helping his people to live better lives?

He had met his test of leadership. But Sir William had said that was not enough. There were other things . . . The time to talk of them had come now, Joseph thought. He considered going to Mount Johnson, but Mohawks returning from there brought word that the baronet, very busy with his work as superintendent of Indian affairs, was absent much of the time in Albany.

One August afternoon, however, as he returned to the village after a ramble in the forest, Joseph was met by his step-father.

"I have been looking everywhere for you, Thayendanegea," Carrihogo said. "Warraghiyagey is waiting for you in the council chamber."

Joseph was off with a bound. In the council hall Sir William and Little Abraham squatted on the ground smoking their pipes. With them was a third Indian of slight build with serious, intelligent eyes.

Sir William rose and came forward. "My brother!" he exclaimed. He spoke in Mohawk but held out his hand in the white men's way of greeting. "I am glad to see you!"

"I am honored that you have come," Joseph replied. "I have wished many times that I could see you and ask your counsel."

"I want you to meet one of our brothers of the Montauk tribe who live on the large island in the sea that is called Long Island," said Sir William. "Joseph, this is David Fowler." And in English he said, "David, this is Lady Johnson's blood brother, Joseph Brant."

Little Abraham then took his departure and the others sat down. Sir William, speaking in Mohawk again, said, "Yes, it has been a long time since we talked together, but I did not forget my promise. Nor have I forgotten that just before the battle near Fort Niagara you kept some of our brothers of the Hodenosaunee from deserting to the French."

Joseph stared in amazement. How had Sir William heard of it? Perhaps word of what he had done had reached Little Abraham, who had spoken of it to the baronet.

"It was a brave act," Sir William went on. "The Indians and the British light infantry broke up the enemy's flank attack on Colonel Massey's breastwork. If the warriors had not remained loyal, the French might have succeeded. I am proud of you, Joseph. You proved yourself a leader as well as a warrior."

Sir William puffed on his pipe as Joseph, pleased but abashed at such praise before a stranger, sought in vain for a reply.

"I feel certain that you will become a great leader of your people," the baronet went on. "But there are other things you must learn if you are to show them the way to a better life."

"How can I learn, Warraghiyagey?" the young warrior demanded eagerly.

"You must be educated," Sir William replied. "That is why I came here with David Fowler. David is a teacher." He glanced at the Montauk. "Tell Joseph what you have been doing, David."

The Indian from Long Island smiled at the young Mohawk. Joseph liked his friendly manner. "I have been on a mission to the Oneidas to teach them the story of the white men's God," Fowler explained, speaking in the language of that tribe, which the Mohawks could understand because it was almost like their own. "I was sent there by Eleazar Wheelock, the head of Moor's Indian Charity School at Lebanon in the province of Connecticut."

"For a long time I have been hoping that some young men of the Hodenosaunee might attend the Indian Charity School," Sir William interposed. "Now it has been arranged. Mr. Wheelock has agreed to take you and two other Mohawk boys as students. David is here to go with you to Lebanon."

Joseph's head was in a whirl. The thought of going to school and getting away from the things he disliked in the long house was exciting.

"What will I do at the school?" he asked.

"You will learn to speak English and to read and write it," David Fowler explained. "And you will be taught the ways of civilization and how to cultivate the land."

The young Mohawk looked thoughtful. To learn English would be fine. It would be very useful. But cultivating the land . . .

"Do you mean I must go into the fields too?" he asked. "But that is squaws' work!"

"Among civilized people it is not considered squaws' work, my brother," Sir William said. He pointed through the open door of the council chamber toward the fields where the squaws were working. "When you have learned the white men's ways, you can teach your people to make their land produce more food. This is your chance to help your people."

Work on a farm! Joseph could see that school would be very different from the warpath. And yet what his people needed most was to learn how to grow enough food to last through the winter.

He was beginning to see that the worthwhile things in the world are often only to be had by doing disagreeable or difficult tasks.

"I will go to the school in Lebanon, Warraghiyagey," he said.

The sight of Indians from several different tribes was nothing new to the people of Lebanon and they had often seen David Fowler. Nevertheless heads turned to stare curiously as the four Indians came into the village. In the lead were David and Joseph, striding along as straight and erect as pine trees. Both wore full Indian dress of tunic, kilt, leggings and moccasins, the Montauk's of cloth and his companion's of deerskin. Behind them the two Mohawk boys slouched along, naked save for their breechcloths and moccasins.

The inhabitants did not stare for long, however. Lebanon was a busy place. Along a stream that ran through the village mill wheels were turning. Everywhere Joseph Brant heard the clang of anvils, the screech of saws, the tap of hammers, and the clunk of looms.

Red eyes glowered at him from within the smoky interior of a shop. David Fowler, noticing his wondering look, said, "That is a forge. They are making axes to fell trees, hoes to work the land, and scythes to cut hay in the meadows."

The Montauk also pointed out shops where cloth, leather, shoes, saddles, harness, and barrels were made.

Already a little homesick, Joseph thought of what the people would be doing back in Ganegahaga. Right now, in the heat of the August day, many of the warriors would be sleeping, others lolling in the shade smoking their pipes and boasting to each other of their deeds on the warpath, or splashing and cooling themselves in the big pool in the river close to the village. No one would be working except the squaws toiling among the corn, beans, and squashes under the blazing sun, using their crude stone implements. His mother would be there, her work-worn body bent over the crops . . .

In Lebanon the sun was hot too, but all the men seemed to be busy.

Now the four Indians were passing the tree-shaded village green. David Fowler pointed ahead. "There is the school," he said.

Joseph's heart sank. He had expected . . . well, he didn't know just what. He had had a vague idea that the school would be large and imposing. But as his eyes followed David's pointing finger he saw a fairly good-sized house with a smaller one beside it, their sides of rough-hewn timbers weathered to a silver-gray. Behind them was a large garden.

David Fowler led the way to the smaller building. "This is Mr. Wheelock's house," he said. "He will want to see us before we go into the schoolhouse."

On the ground floor Fowler pointed to a spacious room with rows of benches and a pulpit in it. "That is the chapel," he said. "And this smaller room is Mr. Wheelock's office."

At his knock a voice from within boomed, "Come in!"

From behind a writing table a handsome, dignified man in a dark blue suit and a large gray-powdered wig rose as the four Indians entered. In English, David introduced the three Mohawks. Then he translated Mr. Wheelock's reply.

"The head of our school bids you welcome and asks you to be seated."

Joseph, who had become accustomed to sitting in chairs on his visits to Mount Johnson, took a seat beside David, but the two Mohawk boys squatted on the floor.

Then Mr. Wheelock spoke again and the Montauk Indian translated: "He hopes you will be happy here. Both he and the teachers want to help you in every way they can, and he asks that if you are unhappy or troubled at any time you will come to see him."

For a moment Mr. Wheelock's gaze rested on Negyes and Center, the two younger Mohawk boys. His forehead became furrowed and he said something to David Fowler, who nodded but did not translate the words. With the little English that he knew, Joseph made out that the head of the school had told the Montauk to see that the boys were provided with clothes—and a bath. He was glad that in spite of the hot weather he was fully dressed and that he had always liked to keep himself clean and neat.

Mr. Wheelock rose, smiling, and as the three new students, following David Fowler's example, stood up too, he shook hands with them. Then, with the Montauk leading the way, they left the building and went over to the schoolhouse.

Its first floor contained a dining hall and kitchen and several rooms used for classes. On the second floor was a single large chamber, which served as a dormitory. David Fowler pointed out the beds the newcomers were to occupy. Negyes and Center scowled at the strange contrivances.

"I will see you in the dining hall when the bell rings for supper," David said to Joseph. And beckoning to Negyes and Center, he took them downstairs. The boys cast forlorn looks at the older Mohawk as they went along.

Joseph sat down on his bed. There was no one else in the dormitory. Everything was so strange and new to him that for a moment he had an impulse to walk out and start the long journey toward home.

The pealing of a bell on the roof of the schoolhouse brought him back to Lebanon and the school. He got up and went downstairs. The students and their teachers were coming out of the classrooms and going into the dining hall. Joseph followed. Inside, he saw David with Negyes and Center. The two boys' faces had a freshly scrubbed look, and they looked very uncomfortable in breeches and knee-length frocks of towcloth.

All three took seats at a long table next to David Fowler. He introduced them to one of the teachers who sat on his other side, a pleasant-looking young man named Charles Jeffrey Smith. Mr. Smith did not speak Mohawk, but David acted as interpreter when the teacher pointed out some of the other students. There were about twenty-five in all. Most of them were Delawares and Mohegans, with a Pequot and a Narragansett or two among them.

Everyone seemed to be talking at once. Joseph wondered how they managed with the different languages. "The students are encouraged to speak English," David Fowler said. "In that way Indians of one tribe can talk to those of another and use what they have learned in classes during the day."

Supper was hasty pudding and milk. Although it was made from ground corn like the sagamite the Indians were so fond of, it seemed to taste different, and since the Six Nations Indians did not keep cows, the milk was new to Joseph but he liked it.

After supper the students filed over to the chapel in the other house, where Mr. Wheelock conducted prayers. They were in English and Joseph could not understand much of them. That night, in the unaccustomed softness of a bed with a mattress and pillows stuffed with feathers, he tossed sleeplessly for a long time. He wondered whether he could stick it out. Then he thought of Negyes and Center. They had looked homesick and frightened at supper and had taken no part in the conversation.

He was older, seventeen. They would look to him as a leader, and he had to set them an example. Not only that, but he must stay and learn so that he could help his people at home. He set his jaw hard.

There were more prayers before breakfast the next morning; then school began. Joseph found himself seated on a bench beside Negyes and Center in a beginners' class in English taught by David Fowler.

The Montauk handed each of the three new students a flat piece of wood, shaped something like a hand mirror, with a handle. On it, under a transparent sheet of horn, was a paper with rows of black marks.

"This is a hornbook," said David. "Those marks are the letters of the English alphabet. When you have learned them, you will begin to put the letters together to make words and sentences. I will point to each letter in turn and pronounce it. You will say it after me."

He went over the alphabet several times with each boy. Then he gave each a copybook, a quill pen, and an inkwell.

"Write the letters in the copybook just as they are formed on the hornbook," he told them. "Go slowly and try to pronounce each letter as you copy it. When you finish, start over again until you are sure you know how to write each letter."

Joseph spent the rest of the morning holding the quill with awkward fingers, laboriously tracing the alphabet in his copybook. When David Fowler came to look at his work a little before dinnertime, he nodded encouragingly.

"You have done well," he said.

Joseph was very happy to think that he was making progress. But that afternoon, when the students went into the fields in back of the school, he was less pleased when Mr. Smith handed him a hoe and showed him the right way to cultivate the corn growing there.

Beside him Negyes grunted and threw his hoe on the ground;

Center did the same. Mr. Smith tried to show them in sign language that they must hoe the corn. The two boys made no move to pick up their hoes but stood scowling blackly at the teacher.

"This is squaws' work," Negyes said in the Mohawk tongue. "I will not do it."

Mr. Smith could not understand, but David Fowler, cultivating a squash patch nearby, did. He came up to the Mohawks.

"You must always do as the teachers tell you," he explained to the two boys. "Mr. Wheelock is a fine man and loves his brothers the Indians, but he is stern when rules are broken. You must hoe the corn, my brothers, or he will have you whipped."

Grudgingly both boys picked up their hoes and went to work, still sullen and muttering. Joseph threw off his tunic and began his hoeing too, but he was glad his friend Ohrante could not see him. He could picture the young Onondaga warrior's scorn.

David Fowler finished cultivating the squash patch and began to hoe alongside Joseph. The afternoon was hot and when the Mohawk stopped to rest for a moment he looked up at the corn, which was nearly ready to harvest.

"What fine corn this is!" he exclaimed. "It is much higher than ours grows and there are more ears and bigger ones. The land here must be very rich."

"Your land in Ganegahaga is just as good," the Montauk replied. "The Indians do not know how to cultivate as well as the white men. They have not learned to use the droppings of farm animals to enrich the land either. And they do not know that raising the same crop on the same land each year exhausts the soil after a while. From time to time it is best to grow a different crop."

Joseph, still gazing wonderingly at the tall corn, had never heard of the things David Fowler spoke of. If he could learn how to do them and then show his people . . .

After that he worked with a will at his hoeing.

From a bench where he sat in the schoolroom Joseph could look out of the window into the golden sunshine of a morning in May. Just across the road that ran past the schoolhouse he saw the bright flash of a bluebird's wing. Somewhere in the woods beyond, a woodpecker was drumming a brisk tattoo and a thrush caroled its ringing song.

In the classroom Aaron Occum was reading in English from the *New England Primer*. The rest of the class was supposed to be following his recitation, but Joseph's attention wandered in spite of all he could do to concentrate. Aaron, a Mohegan from Connecticut, had entered the school a year before Joseph, but he was so backward that he was still with the beginners. He read very slowly, stumbling over the words.

Joseph thought of spring days like this at home that he had spent in hunting, fishing, roaming the woods, or playing ball. How he wished he could be enjoying them now.

At last Aaron came to the end of the verses in the *Primer* that illustrated the English alphabet. The last one was for the letter Z:

> *"Zaccheus, he*
> *Did climb a tree*
> *His Lord to see."*

He was silent a long time before he tried to pronounce "Zaccheus." When he finally did try he could not get the word out.

Someone in the class laughed. Others followed the leader and laughed too.

Aaron Occum stopped. His black eyes blazed with anger and his coppery face became a shade redder. He slammed his book on the floor and stamped on it. Then he flung a curse in Mohegan at his tormentors and ran from the schoolroom.

The class was in an uproar. Mr. Smith held up his hand. "Silence!" he commanded. "We will go on with the lesson, my young brothers. I will talk to Aaron later about the sin of losing his temper. Joseph Brant, you will please read the alphabet verses again, starting with A."

Joseph got up and began:

> *"In Adam's fall*
> *We sin-ned all."*

He read clearly and well, better than any other student in the class. But when he reached the last verse he thought suddenly of Aaron and the trouble the Mohegan had had with it. Joseph knew perfectly well how to pronounce "Zaccheus," but for the life of him he couldn't get the word out either.

Someone snickered and once more there was laughter. Joseph felt the hot blood mounting to his face. An unreasoning anger seized him. Like Aaron, he was on the point of flinging down the book and storming out of the room. But something held him back.

He heard Mr. Smith's voice. "Mr. Wheelock and all the teachers in this school know that our brothers the Indians are a proud and sensitive people. We are careful at all times to avoid hurting your feelings. Yet you yourselves have hurt the feelings of two of your brothers. I am ashamed of you."

When classes ended at suppertime Joseph, too angry to be hungry, went upstairs to the dormitory. When the meal was over David Fowler came to look for him.

"I missed you in the dining room," the Montauk said. He

glanced at a bundle Joseph was tying up with a leather thong. "Why, you have packed up all your belongings as if for a journey!"

"I am going home!" Joseph burst out. "I can't stand it any longer. I am a man, not a boy. I am a warrior and have been on the warpath. How can I stand it here? It is like being in the white men's jail."

The Montauk sat down on the bed. "I know how you feel," he said. "It was very hard for me when I first came here too."

"We must get up before sunrise for prayers each morning," Joseph went on. "Then we must listen while the Bible is read and questions are asked in the catechism. We must pray when it is ended and we must pray after supper before we go to our rooms to study. I want to go hunting and fishing. I want to be a warrior again. I want to be free!"

David put his hand on Joseph's. "At first I missed hunting and fishing too, and swimming in the sea that is on every side of Long Island. I wanted to go home, but I am glad I stayed."

"Why, David?"

"Because what I have learned here will make it possible for me to help my people live better and happier lives."

"I want to do that too!" Joseph said eagerly. "But sometimes it seems hopeless. Most of the boys who come here have no clothes except the old ragged ones they are wearing. They do not even want good ones. You have seen how angry they get when Mr. Wheelock tries to give them new clothes. And many are always dirty."

"That is true," said David. "But they can be taught better ways if their teachers are patient."

"What about Isaiah Uncas of the Mohegans? He can't learn anything. Mr. Wheelock had to put him to work on the school farm. What about the boys who sneak out at night? And most of the students don't stay at the school even as long as I have.

If these boys, who have been chosen to come here, cannot be taught or will not obey the rules, what hope is there for the rest of my people?"

"Try it a while longer," David urged. "You will never be sorry, I promise. Do you want to go home and face your brothers of the Mohawks, who will know that you have failed?"

Joseph realized then that even though he had packed his things he could not have gone home. His pride would have kept him from it, just as it had kept him from storming out of the schoolroom that afternoon. He did not want to fail at anything he set out to do.

"I will stay," he said.

There was no fireplace in the chapel but it was warmer than it would be in the long house at Ganegahaga, Joseph knew. Outside, through the chapel windows, he could see the snow drifting down over Lebanon.

He knew that he should be paying attention to Mr. Wheelock's sermon on this Sunday morning in February, but his mind kept wandering to other things.

He had been at Moor's Indian Charity School a year and a half now. In time, he had felt, he would get used to the daily grind, but he hadn't. He thought of Negyes and Center. A few weeks after they had come to the school, Negyes had fallen ill and Mr. Wheelock had had to send him home. Center had gone along to take care of him on the journey. Neither boy had come back . . . Sometimes Joseph wished he could have gone with them.

Of course, there were good things. He was learning English rapidly. The teachers no longer had to use sign language to make him understand what to do. With his good friend David Fowler he held long conversations in the white men's language. And on Sundays like today he could understand Mr. Wheelock's sermons.

He liked them. Mr. Wheelock was a minister of the Congregational Church, which the Puritan settlers had established in America. But Mr. Wheelock didn't preach as he would have to white men. He told the young Indians stories from the white men's Bible, the Word of God. Many were exciting, like the stories of David and Goliath, Daniel in the lions' den, and about the bloody wars that were fought in those ancient times.

Joseph was startled as he heard Mr. Wheelock speak his name. For an instant he thought the minister was going to reprimand him for day-dreaming. But Mr. Wheelock was telling a story about another Joseph, and how, more than three thousand years before, he had been sold as a slave into Egypt. Then, by interpreting the ruler Pharaoh's dream of seeing seven lean cattle devour seven fat ones, he had saved Egypt from famine.

"The seven fat cattle were seven years of good crops and the seven lean ones years of poor harvests that followed," said Mr. Wheelock. "This story teaches us that in good times we should save for the coming of bad times."

Joseph listened eagerly to the story of his namesake of ancient days. When the service was over, he said to David Fowler, "What a wonderful book the Bible is! It has great wisdom. I wish my people could know the story of Joseph. Perhaps if they did they would use their stores of food more sparingly and not eat more than they want at feasts."

"Why don't you translate the Bible into the Mohawk language?" David suggested.

The young Mohawk was thoughtful. "It would be very hard," he said at last. "My people would have to be taught how to read it too. But I will do it some day, David."

"And since you find the Word of God so wise and truthful, why don't you accept Him and join the church?"

They had reached the schoolhouse. Joseph was silent until they had seated themselves in the dining room. Then he said, "I will think about it. Is it not true that those who join the church must obey the commands that are written in the Bible?"

David smiled but his eyes were serious. "They should do their best," he replied. "God is angry if His children do not try to obey His Commandments."

"I would want to be sure I would always try my best," Joseph said slowly. "I would not want God to be angry with me."

A few days later Joseph Brant made his decision. The following Sunday, before the others in the school, Mr. Wheelock baptized him. For the rest of his life he was to be a devoted Christian. If he failed at times to live up to the Bible's Commandments, perhaps he should not be blamed too sternly. Although he may have had white blood he had been born an Indian. But he tried to live up to his religion.

Joseph Brant became one of the best students the school had ever had. He learned many things that were to be valuable to him in later life. But he was not happy. When the summer of 1763 came he had been in Lebanon two years and was twenty-one years old. One hot, drowsy day it seemed to him that he would give anything in the world to be free, to be home again, and to go for a swim in the cool green waters of the Mohawk River. That afternoon he went to see Eleazar Wheelock.

The head of the school rose from his writing table as the young Mohawk came in. "Welcome, my young brother," he said. "It is always a pleasure to see a student who is such a credit to our school."

As Joseph looked at him he almost wished he had not come. How could he express what he must say?

"I did not want to come here today," he said, "but I know that you understand the ways of the Indians and that you will understand why I must leave the school. I feel I have learned what I need to know to help my people and lead them. I have been here two years and I—I——"

"You cannot stand it any longer, Joseph?" Mr. Wheelock

smiled, but there was deep disappointment in his eyes. "You have done well here and you are very different from most of the others. I had hoped . . . but I understand, my young brother. You are a man and impatient to go out into the world and make your way."

He was silent for a moment, then his eyes lighted up. "Perhaps God meant this to be," he continued. "Charles Jeffrey Smith is to set out in a few days on a mission to the Mohawks. He does not speak their language well and needs an interpreter. You could not only be helpful to him but do great good among your people. Will you go with him?"

Joseph was pleased. Here was an opportunity he had long wished for. Charles Jeffrey Smith was an understanding teacher. He would be loved and respected by the Indians, just as Sir William Johnson was.

"I will go, Mr. Wheelock," Joseph replied.

Chapter 5

Sir William's great stone mansion at Mount Johnson was standing silent and deserted when Joseph and Charles Jeffrey Smith reached it after their long journey. After making inquiries of nearby settlers, they pushed on to the settlement of Johnstown, farther up the Mohawk River and a short distance inland. Here the baronet had recently built and moved into Johnson Hall, an even more magnificent house.

The two travelers received a warm welcome from Sir William and Molly, and later the three men retired to the baronet's study, where he offered them tobacco and they lighted their pipes. He nodded in understanding when Joseph, speaking pridefully in English, told him why he had left the school. But his face clouded and he shook his head when Mr. Smith spoke of their mission.

"I am glad you came here first before going on to the castles of the Mohawks," he said. "As a white man, Mr. Smith, it would be dangerous for you to go among them."

His words stunned Joseph, who cried, "What is the matter, Warraghiyagey?"

Sir William rose and motioned his two visitors to the window, pointing with the stem of his pipe as they looked out.

"When you came along you may have noticed those two stone blockhouses, one at each end of the house," he said. "I had them put up after Johnson Hall was completed because I feared an attack."

Again he pointed with his pipe stem, this time into the distance toward the west. "Pontiac, the great chief of the Ottawas, who lives on the shores of the great lakes that lie far toward the setting sun, has declared war on the English. He has succeeded in getting the warriors of the other tribes of that region to join his braves."

"But I do not see—" Mr. Smith began. "The Great Lakes are far away. Why should it be dangerous for me to go among the Mohawks?"

Sir William asked his visitors to be seated again. Then he said, "Pontiac is a powerful chief and much to be feared. He hopes to drive all the white settlers from America. By an act of treachery he tried to take the fort at Detroit. Although it was discovered in time, his warriors are now besieging it."

He puffed on his pipe a moment, his face stern. "Pontiac knows he cannot win without the support of other tribes. But he is a great speechmaker and his tongue is oily. He has been trying to get the Six Nations to join him. Already some of the Senecas have listened to him and have taken the warpath. The rest of the tribes are restless. If something is not done to oppose Pontiac, the war may spread throughout the Long House of the Hodenosaunee."

A long discussion followed. At last Charles Jeffrey Smith reluctantly agreed that his mission would have to be postponed.

The next day Mr. Smith started back to Lebanon. Joseph, undecided as to his future, remained at Johnson Hall several days. There was much to talk over with his sister, for he had been away two years. Later, he decided, he would go to Ganegahaga to see his mother and stepfather. But after the civilized life of the school he dreaded the thought of remaining in the long house with all its discomforts and privations.

The news of the war in the west was as disturbing to him as it was to Sir William. In the baronet's study the two discussed the subject again a few days later. Sir William had a proposal to make.

"You have done well at Mr. Wheelock's school, Thayendanegea," he said. "Your English is excellent and you have learned much of the white men's civilization. Now you will have an opportunity to use that knowledge among your people."

Joseph leaned across the writing table toward the baronet, his dark eyes intense. "But how can I do that if there is to be war?"

Sir William's jaw was set hard. "There must be no war in the Long House," he said. "I am determined to see that our brothers remain at peace. You must help me to do it, Joseph."

"How can I help?"

"At Lake George you met the test of courage in war," the baronet replied. "At Fort Niagara you also proved yourself a leader in war. Now you must meet the hardest test of all—the test of a statesman."

"A statesman?" Joseph repeated with a puzzled air. "That is a word I have not heard before."

"The English call a leader in peace a statesman. I am going to ask you to be a statesman among the people of the Hodenosaunee."

He gazed for a moment into Joseph's questioning eyes. Then he went on: "In a few days I shall make a journey up the river to sit in council with the chiefs and warriors of the Mohawks and explain why they should remain at peace and not be misled by Pontiac's false words. But since I must travel eastward to Albany soon I cannot continue on to the castles of the Oneidas, Onondagas, Cayugas, Senecas, and Tuscaroras. You must go in my place, Thayendanegea."

Joseph was silent for some moments, his brow furrowed. Then he said slowly, "You have told me that the great chief Pontiac is wrong, but I do not know why. You say that Pontiac seeks to unite all the tribes. It was by uniting into one Nation that the Hodenosaunee became strong in war and feared by their enemies. Would it not be a good thing for all the tribes in America to unite in one Nation?"

"For peace, yes—but not for war," Sir William agreed. He smiled at the young warrior. "Before you go we shall talk of this again. I will show you why it would be wrong for the Hodenosaunee to join with Pontiac's warriors against the English."

On his journey Joseph planned to go first with Sir William to Ganegahaga, where he would stop a few days to see his family. Before they started, he and the baronet had several long talks. And because he loved and trusted the great and powerful friend of the Indians, the Mohawk was convinced that he should undertake the mission among the other tribes. Yet in his heart he still had certain doubts . . . Could Pontiac be right in his belief that the English must be driven from America? What was going to happen as more settlers pushed into the Indians' lands and hunting grounds? Would they treat the red men fairly? The Six Nations could trust Warraghiyagey, yes, but what of other leaders of the white men in America?

The young Mohawk's heart sank as he came through the stockade gate into Ganowalohale, the principal village of the Oneidas on the eastern shore of the large and beautiful lake named for this tribe that lived along its shores. The village itself looked peaceful enough in the sunlight of the September afternoon, with the smoke of cooking fires curling up from the long houses. But Joseph's keen eye did not miss a tomahawk, painted red and ornamented with red feathers and black wampum, stuck in a pole at the center of the village. Red was for blood, black for death to the enemies of the Oneidas.

A young brave came out of one of the long houses. Joseph went up to him.

"I am Thayendanegea of the Mohawks," he said. "Go to your war chief, Conogquieson, and tell him I will await him in the council chamber. Say that I bring an important message from Warraghiyagey."

The Oneida did not look pleased, though he went off quickly enough at the mention of Sir William's name. And it was some time before Conogquieson appeared.

The two warriors faced each other in the otherwise deserted council chamber. They were as different in appearance as two Indians could be—Joseph Brant tall and straight, with a bearing that was somehow kingly, his gaze direct and dignified; the Oneida chief short and lean, with a bullet head and hatchet-like features, the black eyes as dull as a snake's.

The Mohawk handed the war chief one of the belts of white wampum he had brought on his journey. White was for peace.

"By this token of his love and esteem for his brothers War-raghiyagey greets them and expresses his desire for peace in the

long houses of the Onayotekaono," he said, using the Oneidas'
Indian name.

Conogquieson's greeting in reply was not cordial. "You are
too late," he said. "The warriors are preparing to join the great
chief Pontiac and drive the English into the sea. You saw the
tomahawk on the war pole."

"I saw it," Joseph replied, "but it is not too late. It is Warraghiyagey's wish that you call a council of all the chiefs and
warriors so that I may give them an important message from
him."

Again he was thankful that he had come as the representative
of Sir William. He saw Conogquieson's eyes glitter with dis-
pleasure, but he knew the Oneida dared not refuse the baronet's
request.

"I will call the council but it will do no good," the chief replied. "The war belt has been cast upon the ground and snatched
up by the warriors. The war dance has been held."

Later that afternoon, standing before the hostile gaze of the
Oneida chiefs and warriors, Joseph Brant made his plea for
peace.

"Brothers!" he cried, "you know that Warraghiyagey is very
wise and that he always speaks the truth to his brothers of the
Hodenosaunee. He has sent me to tell you not to listen to the
false counsel of Pontiac, for if you do you will surely be destroyed."

He paused, his gaze wandering around the close-packed
circle of warriors. Their faces were cruel and sullen as the firelight flickered on them through the haze of smoke from many
pipes.

"Many of you saw the might of our great father the King of
the English when his Red Jackets marched against the French,"
he went on. "You heard the thunder of his big guns. You saw
the thick walls of the French fort at Niagara crumble to dust
before the great iron balls, whose flight is swifter than the

eagle's. If you join Pontiac the King will be angry. He will send armies against us. The Hodenosaunee will all be killed and their villages burned."

When Joseph finished his speech, assuring the Oneidas that they would be fairly treated if they remained friends of the English, a "Ho! ho!" of applause went up from the warriors but there was little enthusiasm in it.

Conogquieson rose to reply. "Brothers!" he shouted, "Warraghiyagey promises us fair treatment by the English if we do not take the warpath, but what of all the white settlers that keep coming? Our lands and hunting grounds grow smaller each year. Is this fair treatment?"

A resentful growl went up from the warriors as he stopped and gazed around the circle.

"The English talk of peace," he continued, "yet what happened when we sent a petition to Warraghiyagey asking that the forts the white men have built in the Long House of the Hodenosaunee be pulled down and kicked out of the way? Nothing! The way for the Indians to obtain peace and justice is to join Pontiac and kill all the white settlers."

He went on, boasting of the victories Pontiac's mighty army would win and the English scalps they would take. When he sat down the warriors' "Ho! ho!" seemed to shake the long house.

The council ended with the usual feast. No one paid much attention to Joseph. Too downcast to be hungry, he wandered out of the council chamber, down to the lake shore. There he sat down on a rock and stared disconsolately out over the water.

He had not known how to reply to Conogquieson's assertion that the Indians were losing more and more of their lands. But he did not think war by a few tribes of Indians would solve the problem. A union of all the Indian nations, however, would be strong enough to win fair treatment without war, he believed.

Absorbed in his thoughts, he did not immediately realize

that someone was standing beside him. Suddenly aware, he looked up into a smiling face. For a moment he thought it was a child, so slight was the intruder's figure. Then he saw it was an Indian girl, somewhat younger than himself.

"Why are you sad, Thayendanegea?" she asked.

Astonished, Joseph demanded, "How do you know my name?"

She was still smiling. He saw that she was not as pretty as his friend Catherine at home, but there was a look in her large dark eyes that made him feel he had found one friend in the midst of the Oneidas' hostility.

"Everyone in the village knows you are here and that Warraghiyagey sent you," the maiden replied. "Many of our warriors have been on the warpath with you. Even before you came I had heard them speak of your bravery in battle." She sat down on the rock beside him. "Why are you sad?" she repeated.

Moodily Joseph picked up a flat stone and cast it out over the water, watching as it skipped along the surface. Then he told the girl what had happened at the council.

"But you will go back to the council chamber and try again, won't you, Thayendanegea?"

Joseph made a hopeless gesture with his hands. "It is no use."

She gazed at him shyly. "But you must tell the warriors that the Pottawattamies and Wyandots have deserted Pontiac and made peace with the English at Detroit."

The young Mohawk stared at the Oneida girl. Was this her idea of a joke?

"How do you know?" he demanded.

"I do not dare tell you that, Thayendanegea, but I have sharp ears . . . Two of our warriors arrived this morning from Kanedesaga, the Old Castle of the Senecas near the great hill of Genundewa. They heard of it from Senecas who returned from the warpath at Detroit. The two tribes became convinced that Detroit could not be taken before heavy English reinforcements arrived. Since Conogquieson is determined to take the warpath, he forbade the two warriors to tell the others of the separate peace."

"The Pottawattamies and the Wyandots!" Joseph breathed. "That means Pontiac has left only his own Ottawas, the Ojibwas, and those of the Senecas who have joined him. He will surely be beaten before any of our warriors can reach Detroit!"

He stood up. For a long moment he gazed out toward the west, where the sun seemed to be sinking into the lake. In its fast-fading light a gleam of triumph shone in his eyes. He could go back to the council chamber now and force the truth from the two Oneidas who had learned of the separate peace. Once the other braves heard of it, he did not think they would take the warpath, in spite of all Congoquieson might say. Indian warriors followed their chiefs into battle only if it pleased them to do so.

Joseph turned back toward the girl. "What is your name?" he asked.

She was still sitting on the rock and again her dark eyes were shy as she looked up at him from under her lashes. "Owaisa," she replied.

"I shall not forget what you have done," Joseph said. And after a moment something made him add, "I shall not forget *you* either, Owaisa. When my mission is completed I shall come back."

Then, with his head high in full confidence, he strode toward the council chamber.

Sobered by the news of the separate peace, the Oneidas did not take the warpath. Joseph continued his journey westward. In a beautiful valley at the center of the lands of the Hodenosaunee lay the principal village of the Onondagas, capital of the Six Nations. Here Sir William's emissary conferred with the chiefs and warriors in the Great Council Hall, where the wampum belts recording all treaties made by the Confederacy were kept. And here too he was reunited with his old friend Ohrante.

He found the Onondaga married to a fat and jolly young woman whose round face seemed always wreathed in smiles. The couple had a small son. Ohrante insisted that his friend stay with them during his visit, and they relived their adventures on the warpath in their many talks.

One day as they sat before the cooking fire during their evening meal, Ohrante spoke of his disappointment that his friend's mission was a peaceful one. "I had hoped we would soon take the warpath together once more."

Before he replied, Joseph's eye wandered first to the papoose contentedly trying to swallow his foot on the earth floor of the long house, then to Ohrante's wife, who was refilling their bowls with sagamite from the kettle over the fire.

"But with a good wife and a little son you should be happy that the Hodenosaunee are at peace," he said wistfully.

"Oh, yes, I am very happy," Ohrante replied, "but sometimes I find peace very dull. What good is a warrior who never takes the warpath? With you it is different, my brother. You have been to school. You speak English and you know the ways of the white men. You go on missions for Warraghiyagey. If I could travel about and see more of the world, perhaps I would not miss the warpath."

Joseph looked sober. "I do not know what lies ahead for us," he said, "but I have a feeling that we shall see more of each other in the future."

More than once, as he went on westward, he thought somewhat enviously of Ohrante and his little family. And although his acquaintance with Owaisa had been so brief, he could not keep the Oneida maiden out of his mind. He wished he might stop by her village on his return journey, but since his final visit took him south of the Oneidas' lands to those of the Tuscaroras he was unable to do so.

Now it was early summer in 1764 and once again Joseph Brant journeyed west. This time, when he reached Ganowalohale he was received cordially by the Oneida chiefs. But since he had not come to sit in council with them, he lost no time in seeking out Owaisa.

He found her in the fields hoeing squash. When his keen gaze picked her out among the other squaws he had a feeling of resentment that one of her frail figure had to work so hard.

The Indian maiden glanced up as Joseph came toward her, but there was no surprise in her dark eyes.

"Did you think I had forgotten, Owaisa?" he asked.

"No, Thayendanegea," she replied simply. "You promised to come and I knew you would."

The young Mohawk took the hoe from her hands and dropped it between the rows of squash vines. "Let us go down by the lake," he said gently. "I have something to tell you."

He led her to the shore and drew her down beside him on the very rock where he had been sitting in despair when they had first met.

"I owe much to you, Owaisa," he said. "What you told me that day turned my mission from failure into success. When I went on I found the warriors of the other tribes preparing to take the warpath for Pontiac too, but they listened when I told them what I had learned from you. Even at the great Seneca castle of Kanadesaga, where the powerful sachem Guiengwatoh and the wily chief Sagoyewatha whom the English call Red Jacket were very hostile, they listened."

"I know," said Owaisa. "We have heard in our village that the Senecas who joined Pontiac have now made peace with the English."

"I had hoped to return here sooner," Joseph went on, "but I have been on the warpath against the Delawares. They also joined Pontiac's alliance and were raiding the English settlements to the south of our tribe's lands. Warraghiyagey sent out a war party of Mohawks to stop them."

"Did you take many scalps?"

In fine scorn Joseph kicked a pebble into the water. "No. The cowardly Delawares ran away when we approached. We burned their deserted villages. Perhaps you have heard that many years ago the Hodenosaunee won a great victory in a war against the Delawares. They have feared us ever since. Our warriors laugh at them, calling them women."

Owaisa sighed. "But I have heard that Pontiac is still fighting the English. Do you think the war will be over soon?"

"Yes, Pontiac's power is broken now." Glancing at her, he added, "You look glad, Owaisa. I am too."

Then he spoke of how he had been at the Indian Charity School. "When I left there," he continued, "there were many things I wished to do but the war interfered."

As the Indian girl listened attentively, he told her of his hopes and plans for making his people's way of life better.

Owaisa's eyes glowed. "What you wish to do is a very wonderful thing, Thayendanegea," she said. Once more she sighed. "How I wish I had been a boy! If I were a warrior I would try to be like you and help my people. But what can a girl do?"

She looked up as she felt his hand on hers. He was gazing straight at her, and her heart leaped at what she saw in his eyes.

"You can do much," Joseph said softly. "That is why I came back to Ganowalohale as soon as I could. There has never been a day since I left here when you have not been in my thoughts. I need you to help me. A man who does not have a good wife is like a courier who sets out on a journey in mid-winter without snowshoes. Will you marry me, Owaisa?"

Her glance was very shy as she nodded. And so it was that, following the ancient Indian custom, Owaisa, her mother and father, her half-sister Onogala, and a younger brother who was still at home journeyed through the forest with Joseph Brant to Ganegahaga.

The night of their arrival there was feasting and dancing in the long house as the members of Joseph's Wolf Clan and those of the Bear Clan, to which Owaisa belonged, welcomed the young couple.

Later, when the bride and her family had gone to the long house in which quarters had been provided for them, Joseph had a few words alone with his mother.

"I am glad for you, my son," she told him. "Owaisa is a fine girl and she will make you happy, I know." Then she hesitated and a shadow crossed her face. "But, Thayendanegea, she is so thin and she does not look well. She will not be able to do the work that a stronger girl could."

Joseph's face, too, was grave. Exhausted after her long journey, Owaisa had not looked well at the feast.

"I feel sure she will be better soon," he said. His face took on a determined look. He was resolved that Owaisa should not become a drudge like most squaws.

As he went to bed that night it suddenly came to him that one face had been missing among the members of the Bear Clan at the feast. He had not seen his friend Catherine, the daughter of Chief Tahkarihoken. He wondered why . . . He could not know that from a distance Catherine had seen him as he came through the stockade gate that afternoon with Owaisa and her family, nor that she had told her father and mother she did not feel well and had remained at home alone that night.

The following morning a small procession filed out of one of the long houses and went toward the one where Joseph's family lived. At its head walked Owaisa, her slight figure gay in its skirted costume embroidered in bright-colored beads and porcupine quills. In her hand she carried several pieces of unleavened corn bread, proof of her ability to cook for her intended husband. Behind her walked her mother and Onogala, also dressed in their best.

Joseph's mother greeted them solemnly. Neither her son nor Carrihogo were present. With a sweet dignity Owaisa handed the corn bread to her future mother-in-law, who in return presented a gift of dried venison to the bride's mother.

And by this simple ceremony Joseph Brant and Owaisa were married.

Chapter 6

For seven busy though uneventful years, Joseph and Owaisa lived in a house he built near the Upper Castle. But his heart was troubled one morning early in 1772 as he stood looking out over the white world of mid-winter in the wilderness. Beyond the snow-covered clearing the frozen river lay silent. Save for the gentle soughing of the wind in a grove of pines that made a green patch among the stark, bare branches of the forest, not a sound disturbed the stillness. The Mohawk warrior's gaze, shifting toward the leaden sky, told him that the clouds held more than wind. It looked and smelled like snow.

He was about to go back inside when something caught his eye. Upstream, beyond the clearing, where the trail to Ganegahaga disappeared into the forest, a tall figure moved toward him with the swaying walk of a man on snowshoes. Through narrowed eyes, Joseph made out that it was no buckskin-clad warrior or fur-hatted white woodsman. The stranger wore a long black greatcoat and black cocked hat and carried a pack over his shoulder.

For his part, as he came closer, the traveler saw in the doorway the stalwart kilted figure of a brave in his early thirties whose headdress held the eagle feather cluster of a Mohawk chief. The two-storied house might have been the snug dwelling of a white settler, built of hewn timbers with a large stone chimney from which smoke was drifting up.

The stranger raised an arm in greeting; then as he approached the door he said in English, "You are Joseph Brant, I make no doubt, since they told me at the Upper Castle of the Mohawks that your house was the first one along the river below their village. I am John Stuart, a minister of the gospel of the Church of England."

The Mohawk extended his hand. "You are welcome, Mr. Stuart. I heard that you were on a mission among my people. I am glad you got here ahead of the storm."

The young minister removed his snowshoes and followed Joseph into the house. Daylight fell only dimly into the single large room on the ground floor through the sheets of oiled paper that served as windowpanes; but a fire crackling cheerfully in its fireplace shed a flickering illumination that showed the visitor two small children playing on the hearth. Beside them a puppy dozed. An iron pot, hung from a crane, bubbled over the fire, speaking of preparations for dinner, and in the center of the room a table was set with pewter dishes.

Joseph took Mr. Stuart's pack, greatcoat, and hat and hung them on a peg on the wall. The minister, standing by the fire, was warming his chilled fingers.

Mr. Stuart pointed toward the two little ones at his feet. "These are your children, I suppose, Joseph," he remarked.

"Yes," the warrior replied. "Isaac, my son, is six, and my daughter Christiania is four. We have given them English names since we want them to know English and learn the ways of the white men."

"And your wife—is she at home?"

A look of deep sadness came into the Indian's eyes. "She is . . . very sick," he said slowly. "It is the disease the white men call lung fever."

As if to confirm his words the sound of a long, racking cough from somewhere above reached the visitor's ears.

Mr. Stuart looked greatly disturbed. "Forgive me for coming here in a time of trouble. I have long wanted to meet you, but I must be on my way now back to my headquarters at Fort Hunter."

He would have put his things on again but Joseph's hand restrained him. "Please stay, my brother," he said. "Owaisa is quite comfortable. I only wish you might meet her. Her half-sister is keeping house while she is ill. So you see, you will not disturb us. Besides, it is beginning to snow. It looks like a blizzard."

In spite of all Mr. Stuart's objections, Joseph insisted that he remain for dinner. He pulled chairs up to the fire and, the minister having refused his offer of tobacco, he lit his own pipe and the two sat down to talk.

"I have heard much of you, Joseph," John Stuart said. "You are doing fine work here among your people."

The Mohawk stared into the bright blaze for a moment. Then he replied simply, "I want to make things better for my people but it is not easy. The Indians are wise in the ways of the forest and the warpath, but they are children in their understanding of the white men's civilization."

"Ah, yes," the minister agreed, "but you are setting them a good example." His gaze wandered about the comfortable room. "Your way of life here is far better than that in the long house."

A grave smile quirked the corners of Joseph's mouth. "I hope that in time all my people will have houses for themselves, but that too is not easy to bring about. When I left the long house, many of the warriors were scornful when they saw me at work building this house and cultivating the crops in my fields. But they are no longer scornful, and I hope in time they will learn that it is better to work and live in comfort."

Mr. Stuart nodded. "I hope so too, Joseph. Chief Little Abraham at the Upper Castle told me that if it is a long winter there will be want in the long house before spring."

Joseph nodded gloomily. "It is the same almost every winter. Since I am now able to raise more food than my family needs I share it with my brothers in the village, but it is not enough."

At Ganegahaga, Little Abraham had told Mr. Stuart of other things Joseph had done to help his people. They held him in great respect and love, the sachem said, and had made him a Pine Tree Chief, an honor given only to distinguished warriors who could not become chiefs by the ancient custom of succession through the mother's side of the family.

While Mr. Stuart and Joseph were talking, the children had been playing quietly on the hearth, babbling to each other in the Mohawk tongue. But suddenly the men were interrupted by shrill yelps of pain from the small dog and the little girl's cries. They saw that Isaac had seized the puppy by the throat and was trying to strangle it.

"Make him stop!" Christiania shrieked. She was beating at her brother with her small fists. "He is trying to kill Tono!"

Her father leaped up and snatched the struggling puppy from the boy's grasp. "Why did you do that, Isaac?" he demanded.

Mr. Stuart's knowledge of the Mohawk language was somewhat limited, but he could not mistake the meaning of the look in Isaac Brant's eyes as he stood glowering at his father. The cold hatred in them made a shudder wriggle up the minister's spine.

Before her brother could reply, Christiania sobbed, "He hurt my little dog! He said he was going to kill him and put him up on a pole!"

Isaac eyed his father sullenly. "Give me back the dog," he said. "We are playing New Year's Jubilee. He is the White Dog and must be sacrificed to Hawenneyu."

Mr. Stuart saw deep distress in Joseph's eyes. "I have told you before that you must not be cruel to helpless animals, Isaac," the warrior said sternly.

"I have seen boys in the village torture dogs," Isaac replied sulkily. "That is how they learn to put captives to the torture when they become warriors. I shall learn to do it too."

"Because other boys do it does not make it right," Joseph said. "I want my son to be different. You must be taught that the white man's way of mercy toward a captive is a better way."

Footsteps coming down the stairs interrupted them. Joseph's gaze shifted from his son's angry face to the Indian woman standing there.

"I want you to meet Mr. Stuart, a minister who has come among our people from Fort Hunter," he said to her in Mohawk as she came toward them. To Mr. Stuart he explained in English, "This is Owaisa's half-sister Onogala."

Like Joseph's wife, Onogala was slightly built and bore a slight resemblance to Owaisa. Though she spoke no English she smiled amiably at the minister and extended her hand shyly in greeting. Then she turned to the Mohawk chief.

"Is something wrong, Thayendanegea?" she asked. "Why is Christiania crying?"

"Isaac has been a bad boy," Joseph told her. He spoke to his son. "You will go with Onogala and stay in your room till dinner."

Onogala took Isaac by the hand and started for the stairs, but he wrenched free and turned toward his father again malevolently. "I hate you!" he blazed. "When I become a warrior I will do as I please. Then if you try to stop me I will kill you!"

When he had gone with Onogala the two men sat down again. Christiania had stopped crying and was holding the little dog in her arms, stroking its head and crooning over it.

Deeply embarrassed, Joseph said, "I am sorry this happened while you were here, Mr. Stuart. Sometimes I am discouraged about Isaac. It is very hard to control him. He loves his mother but he does not love me. He seems to think I am to blame for her illness. I try to be a good father and I do not understand . . ."

There was anguish in his eyes. "My wife has told me her uncle once killed a man of the Onondagas in a rage. Then he was killed in revenge by a relative of the dead warrior, for that is the law of our people. Could it be that the same bad blood is in Isaac?"

Mr. Stuart put his hand on Joseph's shoulder. "Do not worry about it, my friend. The boy is young. No doubt he will change as he grows older." Quickly he shifted the conversation to another subject.

"As you may know," he said, "I have a church at Fort Hunter where I preach to the English and Dutch settlers. I have been learning your language in the hope of beginning a translation of the Bible into Mohawk so that your people can know the Word of God."

"I wish it could be done!" Joseph thought of his promise to David Fowler that some day he would do the same thing.

"It can be done. That is the reason I came here today. Will you come to Fort Hunter, Joseph? I want your help in translating the Bible."

Reluctantly the warrior shook his head. "I would like to but my people need me here. You saw how miserably they live in Ganegahaga. And my wife is too ill . . . I have prayed much to God to make her well again. Do you think He will, Mr. Stuart?"

For a long moment the minister was silent. In spite of his

absorption in the conversation with Joseph, he had been aware
of the continual coughing upstairs. He realized that Owaisa
was very sick with the dread tuberculosis, perhaps even sicker
than the Mohawk chief knew.

"God moves in a mysterious way," he said gently. "We do
not always understand it, but we must have faith that it is for
the best."

Soon afterward Onogala came down again, and when she had
taken Owaisa's dinner up to her they all sat down at the table.
With Joseph acting as interpreter, the three older people chatted
pleasantly. Christiania was very much the little lady, sitting
quietly, her dark eyes turned now and then on the white man
who had come to see her father. Only Isaac remained unfriendly
and ate his diner in sullen silence.

Afterward the minister again spoke of his plans for translating the Bible. It had begun to snow soon after his arrival but
toward mid-afternoon it stopped. Joseph urged him to stay
overnight, but he decided to go on down the river to the white
settlement of Canajoharie.

When he had gone, Joseph went up to Owaisa's sickroom.
A paroxysm of coughing shook her as he sat down on the bed
beside her, took her thin hand in his, and told her of Mr. Stuart's
visit and his invitation to come to Fort Hunter.

"If you could only go, Thayendanegea!" Owaisa said weakly.
"Perhaps when the cold winter is over I will be better and we
can go, my dearly beloved."

Joseph gazed at her with desperation in his heart. She had
always been slight and frail, but now she was wasted to a
shadow. Her dark eyes seemed huge and hollow against the
pallor of her face, whose once-bronzed color was now almost
as pale as a white woman's.

Joseph remembered the happy days that had followed their
marriage, when Owaisa had been proud of the comfortable
house he had worked so hard to build. She had been so eager

to learn the white men's ways of living. After the children were born it had seemed that he could ask nothing more than to live out his life there with his family and to work for the good of his people, with Owaisa to help him.

And he had had such great hopes and plans for his son, of whom he had been so proud. But the boy had returned his love with hate. What, he wondered, would Isaac's savagery lead to?

Far worse than his worries over his son were his fears about Owaisa. She spoke of getting well when the warm days came again. Did she really believe it?

Joseph Brant turned his head away so that Owaisa would not see the despair in his eyes.

Another winter came to the Mohawk Valley. The early twilight of the December afternoon was falling and it had begun to snow when Joseph, following the trail along the river, saw the lights of the stockaded settlement of Fort Hunter, below Johnstown, winking in the distance.

When he reached Mr. Stuart's house the minister came to the door in answer to his knock.

"Joseph!" he exclaimed, "I am so glad to see you! It has been a long time, my brother! Come in and warm yourself."

When he had led his visitor into the parlor and lighted candles there he saw how haggard and worn the Mohawk chief looked.

"Sit down, my brother," he said, "and tell me what brings you to Fort Hunter."

For some moments Joseph did not speak. He sat with his head bowed. When he looked up his eyes were filled with a great sorrow.

Then he said simply, "A year ago you asked me to come here and work with you. I could not do it then. Last spring Owaisa died. I was very lonely after she went, but I stayed in my house and tried to keep on helping my people."

He thrust out his hands, palms upturned, in a gesture of hopelessness. "I cannot stand it any longer. Everything there reminds me of Owaisa. So I have come to you, Mr. Stuart."

"What of your children, Joseph?"

"Onogala has taken them to be with her in the Oneidas' village of Ganowalohale. Perhaps later I may bring them to be with me." He bowed his head again.

Mr. Stuart said gently, "God sends us times of trial to test us, Joseph. You will meet this hard test He has put before you, I know."

Joseph thought of the tests Sir William Johnson had said he must meet if he were to become a leader of his people. He had proved himself courageous in battle and had met the test of leadership. Now the minister was saying that God had sent him the hardest, bitterest test of all. Why? He could not understand . . .

"Time will make this trial easier to bear," Mr. Stuart went on. "And work is the best thing to make time pass quickly. There is much work for you to do here, my brother. If you are ready we shall begin tomorrow."

Joseph Brant raised his head and met the minister's gaze unflinchingly. "I am ready," he said.

Chapter 7

Joseph set to work with a will in the hope that the passing of time would ease his trials. Yet more of them lay ahead.

Under John Stuart's direction his first task was the translation of the Gospel of Saint Mark into the Mohawk language. It was very difficult, for the words of the Bible had to be translated in such a way that his people would understand its stories and great truths. But the work progressed and as the weeks passed he realized that the minister had been right when he said that time would make his sorrow easier to bear.

He found comfort in the religion he had adopted while he was at Mr. Wheelock's school. Sometimes it was hard for him to understand why the white men did not always live up to its teaching. There were settlers and traders in the Mohawk Valley who went to church on Sunday but cheated and abused the Indians on weekdays. Joseph himself took the Bible's Commandments seriously and tried his best to follow them.

In Lebanon he had joined Mr. Wheelock's church, the Congregational. But since Mr. Stuart was a minister of the Episcopal, or English, Church and they were working on the Episcopal prayerbook and catechism as well as the Bible, Joseph now joined the Church of England. He was to remain a member for the rest of his life.

But although he was busy he was still not happy, and he missed his children. In spite of Isaac's hatred, Joseph was confident that his son would learn to love him. How could it come about if Isaac and Christiania remained with Onogala in the Oneidas' village?

In the summer of 1773 Joseph made a journey up the Mohawk Valley, stopping at Johnson Hall to see his sister and Sir William, and then going on to Ganegahaga for a visit with his mother and stepfather. Then he continued westward to Ganowalohale to spend some time with his children. Somewhat to Mr. Stuart's surprise he brought back not only Isaac and Christiania but Onogala too.

"Onogala and I are married," he told the minister. "Since Owaisa's death she has been the only mother the children have known. She loves them and they love her. She is even able to control Isaac's fits of temper. You know that I have wanted them with me, but it seemed wrong to take them from her. Onogala is a fine woman and she will be a good wife to me. We have been married according to the Indian custom, but I am a Christian and I would also like to be married in a Christian church."

Mr. Stuart understood that Joseph could never feel the love for Onogala that he had borne for Owaisa, but within a short time he saw that his assistant had indeed acted wisely. As Joseph had predicted, Onogala was a good wife and mother. And she had a way with Isaac that kept his outbursts against his father in check.

Perhaps, under her influence, Isaac might have learned to love his father if she had been spared. But the following winter Onogala caught a cold that developed into a racking caugh.

Like her half-sister, Onogala had never been strong; but while Owaisa's illness had been lingering, hers was not. The disease progressed swiftly. The snow was still deep over the wilderness of the Mohawk Valley when Onogala died.

Outside the stockade of Fort Hunter the forest was green, the river sparkled in the bright June sun, and the birds sang. It was nearly noon and in the Reverend Mr. Stuart's study the air was stifling. Little beads of perspiration stood out on Joseph's forehead but he did not pause to wipe them away. With prodigious energy he drove his quill across the paper before him.

At last, however, he laid the pen down with a sharp exhalation of his breath.

"It is finished, my brother," he said to the minister.

Mr. Stuart also put aside the quill with which he was writing his sermon for the following Sunday. He rose and came over to Joseph's writing table, his kindly eyes surveying the sheets that lay in five neat piles before the Mohawk.

"I congratulate you!" he said. "You have finished something that will be of great value in teaching your people. I think we have done remarkably well together, Joseph. In less than two years we have completed translating the Gospel of Saint Mark, part of the Acts of the Apostles, a short history of the Bible, an explanation of the catechism, and the much-needed revisions in the Mohawk prayerbook."

He picked up one of the sheets and scanned it. "With your neat handwriting they will have no difficulty in setting the type when these are sent to New York City to be printed."

Joseph mopped his forehead. "Do you expect to start more translations soon?" he asked.

"I wish we might, but the English Church in America does not have the money to pay for printing more at the present time."

"Then would it be possible for me to go to Johnson Hall for a time?" Joseph asked. "The Hodenosaunee are to sit in council there early in July. They are going to present complaints to Sir William regarding their treatment by the settlers. Because I am a chief I feel that I should go."

"Of course you should," Mr. Stuart agreed heartily. "You have earned a vacation. By all means go. When you return we can talk of our future work among your people."

Before returning to Fort Hunter, Joseph also planned to go to Ganegahaga. After Onogala's death his mother had taken Isaac and Christiania. He missed them greatly but he knew how much they needed a woman's care.

Joseph had not seen his sister and the baronet for nearly a year. He found them busy with preparations for the council. Sir William's son by his previous marriage to a white woman, Sir John, and his son-in-law, Colonel Guy Johnson, were also at Johnson Hall with their wives and families.

Sir William's appearance disturbed Joseph. It had never occurred to him that the powerfully built soldier would ever be old. Yet as he looked at his sister's husband he saw that there were tired lines in the baronet's face and that his step no longer had the vigor which had enabled him to march as far as the youngest warriors when he led his armies into battle. Sir William was now nearly sixty years old.

It had been many years since Joseph had seen the baronet's son. For a time John Johnson had been in England, where the King had knighted him. He had also lived in New York City, the provincial capital, and had married there. Sir John was very different from his father. He did not have Sir William's gift for making people like him and his way of speaking was blunt.

All the Indians liked Guy Johnson. As Sir William did, he treated them like friends and brothers. He had the same last name as the baronet, was distantly related to him, and had married his daughter Mary. He was assistant superintendent of Indian affairs and an officer in the provincial army.

A few days after his arrival, Joseph had a long talk with Sir William in the latter's study. "You have done a fine service to your people, Joseph," the baronet began.

"I promised David Fowler I would do it," the Mohawk replied. "I do not know whether David is back with his people, the Montauks, but I have written Mr. Wheelock about my work and he will see that David learns of it."

"Do you hear from Mr. Wheelock often?"

"Not as often as when he was in Lebanon. He has given up the school there and started another for white and Indian boys called Dartmouth College. It is far to the north, many suns' journey up the Long River which flows through Connecticut."

Sir William took up a deerskin pouch of tobacco and offered it to the Mohawk chief. Both men filled and lighted their pipes. Joseph produced his proudly. It was a handsome combination pipe and tomahawk, inlaid with silver, a present from the British government for his service to the Crown during the French and Indian War.

Then Sir William said, "As you must know, our brothers of the Hodenosaunee are restless and have many complaints to discuss at the council. They fear that as more white settlers come they may lose their lands and hunting grounds."

He puffed thoughtfully for a moment. "I shall do all I can to obtain justice for them. Then I will go to visit the tribes and tell them what I have accomplished. When I have written the speeches I will make, if you would translate them into the Indian language it would leave me free for other important matters. Do you think Mr. Stuart could spare you for a time?"

"I am sure he could, and I would like very much to do it, Warraghiyagey." Although Joseph had come to use his own English name at all times except in his dealings with the Indians, and had given both his children English names, he still thought of Sir William by the one the Mohawks had given him, meaning "One-Who-Unites-Two-Peoples-Together."

"I am very busy these days." Sir William's face had become grave. "Trouble is sitting on the horizon like a thundercloud."

"Surely you do not mean trouble between the English and the Indians, Warraghiyagey?"

"It is more serious than that. The American colonies may rise against the King. Trouble has been brewing for some time, especially at Boston in New England."

"Do you mean what happened last winter when some of the Bostonians, dressed like Indians, threw a whole shipload of English tea into the harbor? We heard of that at Fort Hunter."

"That was one of the things that began the trouble," said Sir William.

"Why did the Bostonians throw the tea in the water?" Joseph asked. "Don't they like to drink tea? We sometimes had it at the school in Lebanon and it was very good."

"It was because the sachems of the great council called the Parliament in England put a tax upon tea sold in America. The people of Massachusetts say England has no right to tax them."

"A tax? What is a tax?"

Again Sir William puffed on his pipe as he considered how

to explain. "Suppose," he said, "that you buy land from me and pay ten belts of wampum for it. I tell you that you must give me one more belt, which is for the governor of New York, to help pay the cost of running the government of this province. That is a tax."

"What happened after the people threw the tea into the harbor?"

"The Parliament punished them by ordering that no more ships be allowed to trade with the city until the tea is paid for. And they sent soldiers there to prevent further trouble. The people have refused to pay for the tea. An army is being raised, not only in Massachusetts but in other colonies."

"But surely our great father the King will send a mighty army of Red Jackets to crush them as he did the French!" Joseph cried. "What can the settlers do against so many soldiers?"

"They are determined and they believe their cause is right," Sir William replied. "If war does come, I am afraid it will be a long and bloody one."

"Will you fight for the King, Warraghiyagey?"

Before Sir William could reply a servant knocked to say that Guy Johnson wanted to see him on an important matter.

"We shall talk of this again, Joseph," the baronet said, and put an end to the conversation at that moment.

In the meadow near Johnson Hall six hundred warriors sat like bronze statues as Sir William made his reply to their complaints. Beyond them, at the far edge of the meadow, Joseph could see smoke rising from the cooking fires where the squaws were preparing for the feast that would follow this last day of the council. There would be meat, a treat for the Indians, who seldom had it. Three oxen, a gift from Sir William, were being roasted whole in a pit.

Joseph, seated with the other sachems at the head of the field, glanced up at the speaker. Under the pitiless July sun the baronet's face looked parboiled. He had been talking for two hours.

The Mohawk wished he would stop. Ever since the council had begun, Sir William had been ill with dysentery, a complaint from which he always suffered in the summer. That morning he had been very sick.

"You should not try to make your speech, Warraghiyagey!" Joseph had implored. "Let me read it to the warriors for you."

But Sir William had drawn himself up resolutely. "No, my brother, I must talk to them myself. What would they say if I, who have led them into battle, showed myself to be weak like a squaw?"

Why had he insisted? Why was he so worried about this council? Was it that he feared the warriors might not join his side if the war he had spoken of did come?

Which side would it be? Warraghiyagey was a British noble-man, knighted by the King, and an officer in the King's army. Yet he was a man of the people too, a settler like the other white men in the valley. For whom would he fight if the settlers rose against the King?

Of course, Warraghiyagey would want the Indians on his side. But how would the warriors feel about such a war? Would they fight at all?

As if seeking an answer to these questions, Joseph glanced to his left, where Ohrante sat beside him. Ohrante was a Pine Tree Chief now too. The Onondaga's coppery, impassive face, turned intently upon Sir William, gave no clue.

Joseph's gaze, shifting to his right, fell upon Chief Tahkari-hoken of the Oneidas. He thought of the friend of his younger days, Tahkarihoken's daughter Catherine. Earlier he had asked the sachem about her.

"She is well," Tahkarihoken had replied, "but she did not wish to make the journey here."

"She is married, I suppose," Joseph had pursued.

"No," the Oneida chief replied. "Owathaka is a strange girl. She has refused all offers of marriage."

Joseph's thoughts of Catherine were interrupted by a great shout of "Ho! ho!" from the warriors. Sir William, concluding his speech with a promise to obtain justice for the Indians, was presenting three huge strings of wampum to Little Abraham, the war chief of the Six Nations. The baronet's face was bathed in perspiration and he sat down a little unsteadily.

When the warriors began to move toward the steaming kettles of food, Sir William rose and addressed Joseph: "I am a little tired. I will go back to the house for a while and join the warriors later at the feast."

"Shall I come with you, Warraghiyagey?" Joseph was still worried.

"No, I will be all right. Go and join the others, my brother."

But Joseph stood looking after the baronet as he turned and started slowly toward Johnson Hall. Suddenly he saw Sir William stagger and collapse.

With a bound Joseph was at his side, supporting the sagging figure. "What is it, Warraghiyagey? What is wrong?"

"Help me to the house," Sir William said feebly.

With the aid of Joseph and several others who had seen what had happened, the baronet reached the library and sank into a chair. Molly rushed in.

"Carry him to his bed," she ordered the servants. "Send someone to get Sir John!"

Since Sir William was conscious and able to talk, Joseph left his sister and her husband together. He remained in the house, however, pacing up and down the great hall in terrible agitation, his mind filled with fears and doubts. From outside no sounds of revelry in the meadow reached his ears: the news of the baronet's illness had cast a pall over the feast.

About an hour later a servant came to the Mohawk chief. "Sir William is asking for you," he said.

Molly was at the bedchamber door when he reached it. She did not speak, but one look at her face struck cold despair into Joseph's heart. She took his hand and led him to the bed. The baronet's eyes lighted up when Joseph bent over him, but his voice, as he spoke, was very weak. "Joseph, control your people, control your people. I am going away . . ." His voice trailed off.

A moment later Sir John Johnson, summoned from a nearby settlement where he had gone for the day, hurried in. His father showed that he recognized his son, but he could no longer speak. Within a few minutes he lapsed into a coma.

Sir William Johnson, the greatest friend the Indians had ever had or would ever have among the white men, died that night.

Chapter 8

With Sir William's death it seemed to Joseph that whatever was left of his world, after the other tragedies, had collapsed. So many turning points in his life had been due to the great and powerful friend who had been his guiding star—his becoming a warrior at the age of thirteen, the battles that had tested him, his education at Mr. Wheelock's school.

Now he must go on alone. Even in his dying words the baronet had left him a challenge: "Control your people." This, Joseph realized, he must do. He must control and guide them without his benefactor's help.

He had depended much upon his sister Molly too. Through her, Sir William's interest in him had been awakened. Now, in her terrible grief over her husband's death, Joseph found that his sister looked to him for comfort and hope.

He saw that his days of preparation for leadership were over. There was no one to lean upon now. In the future others would depend upon his strength.

For some weeks after Sir William's death he had no thought of leaving Johnson Hall. Molly needed him, and Sir John and Colonel Johnson, busy with the settlement of the baronet's estate, relied upon his help too.

In accordance with the English custom, Sir John inherited his father's property. There was plenty of room in the big mansion for Molly to remain there if she chose, but it held too many poignant memories of the baronet's last days. It was decided that she would go to live at Mount Johnson, where she would be provided with servants to look after all her wants. And now Joseph began to think of returning to Fort Hunter.

One day, however, he was summoned to Sir William's study. Colonel Johnson was seated before the writing table, busy over a pile of papers. It seemed strange to see him there, Joseph thought, as the colonel looked up. Guy Johnson was short where Sir William had been tall; his features, though pleasant, were sharp in contrast to the baronet's; and unlike Sir William he wore his dark hair powdered.

"You have been very helpful to us all in these sad days, Joseph," the colonel said. "Now I need your help in something else. I have just received word that Governor Tryon has appointed me superintendent of Indian affairs to succeed Sir William. I shall leave Johnson Hall in a few days and return to my own home on the river at Guy Park Manor. Will you come with me as my secretary?"

Taken by surprise, the Mohawk chief was silent for some

moments. Then he said slowly, "What kind of work would I do as your secretary, Colonel Johnson?"

"You will take care of many details that I am too busy to see to myself. There will be translations of letters and documents into the Indian tongue. And you will have much to do with my work of helping your people."

The decision was an important one. Could he be of more help to his people by going back to work with Mr. Stuart at Fort Hunter or by remaining with Guy Johnson? It came to him that he would not have hesitated if the invitation had come from Sir William. Yet in the baronet's place it was his son-in-law's responsibility to see that the Indians were fairly treated by the whites. That, Joseph thought, was his people's greatest problem. It would become even more serious with the coming of more white settlers.

"I will stay and be your secretary, Colonel Johnson," he said, "but first I must go to Fort Hunter and tell Mr. Stuart. Then I would like to make a journey to Ganegahaga."

"Of course you will want to tell Mr. Stuart," Guy Johnson replied, "and you want to see your children, I know. If you wish to bring them to Guy Park Manor we will be glad to have them."

Joseph was gazing out of the window of Sir William's study, which faced the west. He was thinking of his children, but there was something else on his mind as well . . .

"I believe you have decided wisely, Joseph," Mr. Stuart told him. "I shall miss you greatly, but it will be a satisfaction to know that you are devoting yourself to the welfare of your people. They need help so badly. And remember that you have a friend here who stands ready to help you and who will never forget you."

His mind relieved, Joseph journeyed on to Ganegahaga. It was good to be at home again. His mother, summoned from the

fields, bustled about preparing a bowl of sagamite for him while
he sat on the floor and talked. She and Carrihogo had not come
to the council at Mount Johnson, and although they knew of
Sir William's death they were both anxious to hear all that had
happened since and about Molly's plans and his own.

The children seemed well and happy. Christiania made no
secret of her joy at seeing her father, but Joseph's heart sank
when Isaac greeted him with a scowl and muttered terse replies
to his questions. A few minutes later the boy took up one of
the curved rackets the Indians used in their game of ball that
became our modern game of lacrosse, and went out without a
word.

Joseph's mother, seeing the sadness in his eyes, said, "Isaac
is like you were when you were nine years old, Thayendanegea.
He thinks of nothing but ball."

Carrihogo shook his head. "Your mother makes excuses for
Isaac," he said. "She loves him because he is your son, but it is
hard to control him. He is a great trial to her."

Looking at his mother's gray hair and work-worn face, Joseph
felt both a great pity and tenderness. He thought how hard it
must be for her to have the care of the children. While he
wished he might take her and his stepfather out of the long
house, he realized that they would never leave it. When he had
built the house where he and Owaisa lived he had asked them
to come there, but they had refused. They had known nothing
better than the long house all their lives and they were too old
to change their ways.

He told them of his new work for Colonel Johnson. "I hope
I will be able to have the children with me at Guy Park Manor
soon," he added.

When he had finished his sagamite he rose. "There is someone in the village I must see," he said.

He thought, as he went toward the fields where the squaws
were working, of how on another summer day like this he had

gone into the fields at the castle of the Oneidas to claim Owaisa as his bride. That seemed long ago. Then he had been fresh from school. It had seemed that nothing but happiness and success lay ahead . . .

In the cornfield he saw one figure among the squaws that was more lithe and youthful-looking than the rest. The girl was bent over her hoe, her back turned to him, but he knew who she was.

"Owathaka!" he cried.

Chief Tahkarihoken's daughter Catherine turned quickly at the sound of her Indian name. Joseph saw astonishment and a great shyness in her dark eyes. Color showed through the copper of her cheeks.

"I—did not know you were in Ganegahaga, Thayendanegea," she said gravely. Again he saw the shy look as if, like a deer, she would have liked to flee swiftly into the forest. It came to him that when he and Owaisa had lived nearby he had scarcely ever seen Catherine on his frequent visits to the village. He wondered why.

"I have just arrived," he told her. "I came to see my mother and my children, but I wanted very much to see you too. Leave your work for a time, Owathaka, and walk with me by the river."

Without a word Catherine laid down her hoe and came with him. Though she had been scarcely more than a child at the time when they had been such great friends, she seemed little changed now. Her figure was fuller, but she had not grown fat like most squaws and her dark beauty seemed even more radiant in its maturity. One thing about her seemed different, however: once she had always been laughing and gay; today, he realized, she had not smiled at all.

By the river he told her all that had happened since he had gone to Fort Hunter after Owaisa's death. He saw her eyes light up when he spoke of his work with Mr. Stuart and of his hope that as Colonel Johnson's secretary he might help his people.

"Once you told me I would find the way to make our people's lives better," he said. "It has not been easy—so far I have done so little . . ."

"But you will, Thayendanegea!" Catherine cried. "I have always known you would become a great leader of our people."

They had reached a glade beside the cool, dark green waters of the river. In the midday August heat not even the songs of the birds broke the stillness. The surface of the water was like glass.

Joseph halted and faced Catherine, looking straight into her eyes. "Will you help me, Owathaka?" he asked.

She looked bewildered. "But . . . how, Thayendanegea?"

"I have had many troubles since the days when we took part in the Feather Dance together," Joseph said simply. "When Warraghiyagey died it seemed as if I could never succeed without him. You have been much in my thoughts since then. I have thought many times of your faith in me. If you will be my wife, Owathaka, I will never again doubt that I will succeed."

Catherine's eyes were still very grave. "I will be your wife and I will try to help you, Thayendanegea." She paused a moment; then, softly as if she were speaking to herself, she said, "It has been so long . . . and I could not hope . . ."

As Joseph, taking her hand in his, led her back toward the village he knew why Catherine had avoided him. Why she had not come with her parents to the council at Johnson Hall. Why she had refused the young braves' offers of marriage. He had been the only warrior in Catherine's heart. Within him his heart leaped with a great joy.

The next morning Catherine, the daughter of Chief Tahkarihoken, with her mother and two married sisters set out from the long house for the one in which Joseph Brant's mother lived. In one hand she held pieces of unleavened corn bread.

When the ancient, traditional ceremony was over and Catherine Brant went to meet her husband, she was smiling once more . . .

Chapter 9

In a canoe with his bride and his two children, Joseph paddled down the river to Guy Park Manor, near Mount Johnson, and began his duties as Colonel Johnson's secretary.

For Catherine it was a new experience to be in a white man's house with its unaccustomed luxuries and ways of life, but she learned quickly and was happy in her devotion to her husband. Although the two children were not her own, she gave them every affection and care. It was not easy, especially with Isaac, but by taking a gentle but firm hand with the boy she managed to control him.

Joseph was happy too. Once again he had a good wife who loved and had faith in him. And although Isaac remained sullen toward him, he still hoped to win his son over.

Working at Guy Park Manor was pleasant. If he grew bored with being indoors, Colonel Johnson would always allow him to go off hunting or fishing for a day or so. He could work in the tunic, kilt, leggings, and moccasins of the Mohawks, which he preferred to the white man's dress. And he had the satisfaction of knowing that he was doing things for his people's welfare.

Several times Colonel Johnson sent him on journeys westward to the castles of the Six Nations. In this way he became better acquainted with the chiefs of the other tribes. He found that they respected his position as the colonel's secretary, his education, and his experience in the ways of civilization, and sought his counsel.

In his work Joseph often saw dispatches brought by couriers from Albany or from Governor Tryon's headquarters in New York City. Some of them spoke of the unrest among the settlers in the American colonies and of the possibility of war. He saw evidences of it in the Mohawk Valley too. Yet somehow he never really thought war would come. Having seen the might of the King's armies, he found it hard to believe that the settlers would dare rise in rebellion. When the winter passed and there was still no war, he was convinced that the trouble would be settled without bloodshed.

One morning late in April of the spring of 1775 a servant summoned him to Colonel Johnson's office. Johnson's face was very grave when Joseph came in.

"A messenger from Albany has just been here," he said. "England is at war with the American colonies. There have been battles at Concord and Lexington in the province of Massachusetts between the rebels and the King's soldiers."

"Were all the rebels killed or did the Red Jackets spare them as they so often do their beaten enemies?" Joseph asked.

Colonel Johnson frowned. "The reports received in Albany say that the rebels drove the King's soldiers back to their camp in Boston."

Joseph's face did not betray his amazement but he said, "I do not understand. Can that be true, Colonel Johnson?"

"It would seem to be. The King's soldiers are bottled up in Boston by the rebels, who are being reinforced by regiments of volunteers marching from the other colonies."

"Will you take the warpath for the King?" Joseph asked.

"Of course. I may need your help as one of the Mohawk leaders to get the Six Nations to join us against the rebels."

As he spoke the sound of a gunshot came from somewhere outside. Colonel Johnson went quickly to the window and looked out.

"Some hunter in the forest, no doubt," he said. "I wanted to be sure it was not an attack. Many of the white settlers here in the Valley are likely to join the rebellion. Watch carefully as you go about, and let me know if you see any of them carrying guns or acting suspiciously."

The news left Joseph greatly disturbed. But for a time, although many of the white settlers had left their homes to join the army of the American patriots, the Valley remained peaceful.

One day late in June Colonel Johnson sent for him. When Joseph came into his office the colonel went to the door and peered outside. Then he carefully closed it.

He spoke in a low voice. "Say nothing of this to anyone, for —as you know—many of the white settlers are hostile to the English. I have received a letter from the King's governor in Canada, Sir Guy Carleton. He asks me to do all I can to get the warriors of the Six Nations to join his army against the rebels. I am thinking of sitting in council with the chiefs and leading men of all the tribes, but I wanted to talk it over with you first."

"Where would you hold the council, Colonel Johnson?"

"At Oswego. It is far enough away from the settlements so that word of the council will not get around until it is over. By that time I hope to be leading our brothers of the Six Nations against the rebel army."

Joseph agreed that the plan was a good one. With belts of wampum inviting the warriors to Oswego, messengers were dispatched to all the castles of the Six Nations.

"If the Hodenosaunee take up the war belt at the council it may be many suns or even many moons before I can return," he told Catherine. "I do not like to leave you like this but"— he drew up his head and squared his shoulders—"I am a Mohawk warrior."

"Do not worry, Thayendanegea," she replied. "No harm will come to us here at Guy Park Manor, I am sure. I hope you will return soon, but if you do not I will understand."

With a party that included Lieutenant Colonel John Butler of the King's Rangers and Butler's son Walter, Colonel Johnson and Joseph set out on their long journey to Oswego. When they arrived at the Indian camp outside the ramparts of the little British fort on Lake Ontario, Joseph saw a familiar figure in the dress of an Onondaga chief seated before a fire. It was Ohrante.

With true Indian solemnity they greeted each other impassively, but Joseph saw in Ohrante's eye the adventurous gleam he knew so well, and a joyous excitement stirred him.

That evening, over their pipes as they sat by their campfire, the two chiefs spoke of what had happened to them since they had last met on one of Joseph's journeys among the Six Nations, of their wives and children, and of their early adventures on the warpath.

At last Ohrante said, "My brother, the Onondagas know that when we sit in council with Colonel Johnson tomorrow he will ask us to take the warpath with him. Do you think the Hodenosaunee should fight for the King?"

Joseph knocked the ashes from his pipe and refilled it. He was glad Ohrante had brought up the subject. "I do not know whether we should fight at all," he replied. "As the number of the settlers grows larger, our lands grow smaller. When the war is over many more white men will come. We must be strong then or we may lose all we have. If we fight and many of our warriors are slain we shall be weak."

"But soon there will be more white settlers than there are Indians. What can the Hodenosaunee do against so many?"

Joseph leaned forward, pulled a brand from the fire, and lit his pipe. "The tribes of the Six Nations became strong by uniting," he said. "If all the tribes in America would unite they would be very strong. We could gain our rights without fighting."

Ohrante grunted doubtfully. "Do you think our warriors

could forget their ancient hatred for our enemies the Algonquin Nations and unite with them? And how about the Delawares, whom we scorn as old women? As for the Nations whose lands are near the great lakes that lie far toward the setting sun, we hardly know them. They would surely think it was some trick to conquer them."

Joseph sighed. "It would be difficult. But I cannot help thinking that it is the only way the red man can survive."

He would have liked to discuss his idea further but Ohrante, yawning, stretched himself at full length before the dying fire and a few moments later was asleep.

The council began the next morning in the clearing where the Indians were camped outside the fort. Before it started, Colonel Johnson had a long talk alone with Little Abraham, the war chief.

Little Abraham opened the council. The white-haired war chief's costume glittered with bright-colored embroidery and ornaments of beads and porcupine quills. At his throat was a silver gorget presented to him by the British. In singsong tones, applauded now and then by a "Ho! ho!" from his audience, he made a speech of welcome to Colonel Johnson.

Joseph gazed about the wide circle around the council fire. It was a dark day, with scudding black clouds shutting out the sun. The flickering light of the fire brought out the savagery of the copper-hued faces in this assemblage of the most warlike of Indian Nations. They sat motionless and silent, the smoke rising from their pipes to be whirled away by the wind.

As Little Abraham talked, Joseph fell to wondering what it was that the war chief and Colonel Johnson had discussed beforehand. He had a sense of something about to happen, something important . . .

Now Little Abraham sat down. Colonel Johnson, resplendent in his scarlet uniform, acknowledged the chief's welcome. Then he spoke of the might of the Six Nations, whose very name struck terror into the hearts of all other tribes. He urged them to take the warpath for the English. At intervals during his speech he presented strings of wampum to Little Abraham.

Then he took from his pocket a piece of paper, crumpled it in his hand, and threw it into the council fire.

"Brothers!" he continued, "if you doubt that the Red Jackets will crush and destroy the rebels as easily as I crush and destroy this piece of paper, listen! I bring you news of a great victory won by the Red Jackets. The rebels were driven in confusion from a place called Bunker's Hill near the settlement of Boston. If the rebels do not take warning from this and make peace with the King, I promise you they will soon be destroyed!"

Joseph saw that many of the Indians did not join the shout of "Ho! ho!" when the colonel had concluded his speech.

Then Sakayengwarton, known to the English as Old Smoke or the Old King, rose. Long white hair streamed over his shoulders and his bronzed face was seamed with age. He was the wisest and most powerful of the Seneca chiefs, and his word among them was law.

"Brothers!" he cried. "I have heard before this of the Red Jackets' victory at Bunker's Hill over the Bostonians. Is this the destruction of the Americans our brother Johnson promises us?"

Now Sagayewatha, another Seneca chief, stood up. The eyes of those around the council fire rested admiringly on the small, wiry figure in the scarlet coat of a British officer. They envied this elegant reward he had gained for his swiftness as a courier in the service of the King, along with the English name of Red Jacket.

"Brothers!" he shouted. "Why should we fight for the English, who have broken their promises to keep the settlers from taking our lands and hunting grounds? Why should we fight for the Americans either, when we are not sure they will treat us fairly? In this war many white warriors will be killed on both sides. Let us wait . . ."

Red Jacket did not finish the sentence but stood there, his sharp eyes looking out craftily from beneath scowling brows and a towering forehead.

Joseph knew what he meant. His implication was: "Let us wait till both sides are weak and then fall on them, driving the English and the American alike into the sea." The Mohawk chief knew, too, that Red Jacket's plan of treachery did not include himself. The Seneca was a coward who had never taken the warpath. But he had the oily tongue of an orator; his Indian name meant "He-Who-Keeps-Them-Awake." The council listened intently as he continued his speech.

Other chiefs followed Red Jacket. Except for the wily Seneca, all were now friendly toward Joseph—Kaghswughtioni, or Red Head, of the Onondagas, cruel-faced Little Beard of the Senecas, Fish-Planter of the Cayugas, Little Aaron, and Catherine's father, Tahkarihoken, of the Mohawks, and others.

All were cautious. None attempted to rouse the warriors to the fever pitch that would lead to a war dance. Not having made up his mind as to what his people's wisest course would be, Joseph remained silent. In the speeches of the others he sensed a lack of confidence in Colonel Johnson that would never have been shown if Sir William had been there.

At noon squaws entered the clearing bearing a great steaming kettle on a pole. In it were meat and a wooden ladle. The warriors helped themselves ravenously, using only their fingers, until the last bone had been sucked clean of its marrow.

In the afternoon Colonel Johnson rose to make another speech.

"Will he throw down the war belt before us?" Ohrante whispered.

"I do not think so," Joseph replied. "Colonel Johnson knows

the chiefs have not yet made up their minds. If he throws down the war belt and it is not picked up, his power among the tribes will be lost. He is wise enough to wait."

Joseph's surmise was right. Colonel Johnson contented himself with urging the Six Nations once more to join the English against the Americans. Their grievances about their lands would be settled fairly, he promised. But although another "Ho! ho!" arose as he concluded, it was not as loud as the applause for the other speakers.

Colonel Johnson's speech was to end the council, Joseph knew. He started to get to his feet, feeling disappointed. He had hoped that the colonel's speech might clear up the doubts in his mind. But Johnson had failed to convince him that the British cause was right.

Joseph felt Ohrante's hand on his shoulder. "Wait, Thayendanegea! Something else is going to happen."

The Mohawk sat down as he saw that Little Abraham had advanced to the center of the circle again. The aged Indian stood with his hand raised for silence, his keen old eyes surveying the faces of the warriors he had led for nearly twenty years.

Then he spoke: "Brothers! For many moons I have been your war chief, but now in the winter, when the wind howls like a wolk pack outside the long house, the cold is like a knife struck into my bones. My heart no longer sings at the thought of the warpath. I wish to spend the rest of my days in peace by the fire. Brothers, you must choose a new war chief to lead you!"

A buzz of talk began as Little Abraham paused. Warrior stared at warrior in astonishment at the unexpected turn the council had taken. Joseph, wondering with the rest, suddenly realized that this was what Little Abraham and Colonel Johnson had discussed that morning.

Little Abraham was speaking again. "Brothers! It is the ancient custom that the war chief of the Hodenosaunee shall be a Mohawk. Among you here is a chief of my tribe, old in wisdom yet young in years and in strength and courage. While he was only a boy he fought with great bravery against the White Jackets and our old enemies the Algonquins. He has the confidence of Colonel Johnson, whom our great father the King has now appointed to look after his children of our Nations. Brothers, choose for your new leader Thayendanegea, chief of the Wolf Clan of the Mohawks!"

Joseph Brant was so stunned that he scarcely heard the deafening "Ho! ho!" that went up. How could it be? There were older Mohawk chiefs—Little Aaron, Catherine's father, Tahkarihoken . . .

Vaguely he became aware that Ohrante had leaped to his feet.

"Brothers!" the Onondaga shouted. "On the warpath our brother Thayendanegea has the ferocity of the wounded panther, the craft of the fox, and the endurance of a rock! Victory is sure if he leads us in battle! Shout the name of Thayendanegea as war chief of the Hodenosaunee!"

A few others were trying to make themselves heard, but their voices were drowned out in the mightiest shout of all from the throats of the warriors: "Thayendanegea!"

Someone was pulling Joseph to his feet. He saw that it was Ohrante, his dark eyes alight with the affection of their long comradeship.

Joseph, still dazed, half stumbled to the center of the circle. This was the greatest day of his life! A great wave of pride swelled in his heart. He thought of Catherine and Sir William, wishing they might be there to see their faith in him justified and their predictions come true.

For a time he stood humbly, unable to say a word, gazing at the intent warriors surrounding him. All faces were turned upon him and in all but one he saw good will. Only Red Jacket's face was darkened by a scowl. Joseph had never felt anything but scorn for Red Jacket and the Seneca, knowing it, hated him.

Then the Mohawk drew himself proudly erect, his eyes glowing. He was nearly thirty-three years old now, tall, straight, and muscular, with features in which there was far more that was noble than savage.

"Brothers! You do me great honor," he began. "You have asked me to lead you in war. I promise you that if we are to fight I will take up the war tomahawk and never lay it down until, with your help, the name of Thayendanegea is more feared by our enemies than a thunderbolt!"

"Ho! ho!" the warriors shouted.

"But as long as there is peace," he went on, "I promise you I will never stop working to make the lives of our people better. And I will work to make our Nation strong, so that we may always obtain the fair treatment that is our right!"

As Joseph ceased speaking, pandemonium broke out in the clearing. Tom-toms began to beat and the warriors flung themselves into a wild dance about the council fire in tribute to the new war chief of the Six Nations.

One more surprise was still to come. Colonel Johnson advanced into the center and stood beside Joseph, vainly trying to make himself heard. At last the excitement died down a little.

"Brothers!" Johnson shouted. "Messengers from Canada reached Guy Park Manor before I left. The King's governor of Canada, Sir Guy Carleton, and a general of the Red Jackets, Sir Frederick Haldimand, have invited you all to a council in Montreal. We will leave at once. There will be much feasting and many gifts, sent by our father the King to his children of the Six Nations."

His words set off another wild celebration. And in this way ended the greatest day for Joseph Brant.

Chapter 10

Montreal was the biggest and strangest place Joseph had ever seen. The morning after the warriors of Colonel Johnson's party arrived, he and Ohrante left the Indian camp on a plain outside the walls and went into the city.

Walking through straight, wide streets lined with fine stone buildings, they stared at the great throng of people hurrying along. There were priests and nuns in somber black robes, elegant ladies and gentlemen in odd-looking carriages called *calèches* drawn by splendid horses, peasants from the country driving ox carts to market, and a host of others.

Suddenly Ohrante stopped short, pointing ahead to a little cart drawn by a dog.

"A dog that works!" he exclaimed. "He must be very different from the dogs in our villages, who do nothing but get underfoot, fight each other, and steal food. I never thought a dog would be useful for anything—except," he added, "to be eaten, of course."

A buckskin-clad, moccasined *coureur-de-bois* approached, looking as wild and savage as any red man. He scowled at the two chiefs.

Joseph scowled back. "He knows we are Hodenosaunee warriors," he said when the bushranger had gone by, "and I am sure he remembers what we did to the French in the last war."

Just then the Mohawk war chief felt a hand on his sleeve. Turning, he looked into the face of another Indian whose cold

107

black eyes were aglitter with hate. The strange brave hissed something at the two chiefs and then swiftly vanished into the crowded traffic.

"An Abenaki!" Ohrante cried. "Do you know what he said?"

"I think he wants us go home. I suppose the Abenakis and other tribes of our old enemies the Algonquins will take the warpath for the Red Jackets. He must be afraid if we also take up the war tomahawk there will be fewer scalps for him and his brothers."

They saw other Indians as they went along—more Abenakis, Montagnais, Hurons, and some of their own tribal brothers. Finally they reached the market place, a section down by the river in which rude booths and stalls had been set up. The place was jammed with ox and dog carts, whose owners were shouting their wares. There were more fine ladies and gentlemen here, as well as many servants carrying market baskets.

As they turned into one of the rows of stalls, Ohrante clutched Joseph's arm. "Do you see what is here, Thayendanegea? Presents!" He pulled his friend toward some stalls where glittering trinkets were set out. "I was sure the white governor and the general of the Red Jackets would have fine gifts for us. They have put them here so we can choose whatever we like!"

He walked over to a booth where hand mirrors were displayed and picked one up. "I will take this. I have always wanted a magic glass in which you can see a picture of yourself."

He was about to walk away with it when the proprietor rushed up, screeching something in French, which neither young brave could understand. He tried to snatch the looking glass away from Ohrante, who held it out of reach with one hand while he drew his tomahawk with a menacing gesture. A crowd began to surround Joseph and Ohrante, all jabbering in French.

Just then a scarlet-coated officer wearing staff insignia pushed his way through the crowd. "Perhaps I can help you if either of you speaks English," he said.

"I do," Joseph replied. He felt embarrassed, for he knew the mirrors were not gifts for the Indian visitors. He realized suddenly that here was one of the weaknesses of his people. They were like children, wide-eyed, too ready to believe in all they saw and heard. Even Ohrante, an Onondaga chief . . .

"What is the trouble?" the Englishman asked.

Joseph told him and the young officer smiled. "Permit me to make you a present of the looking glass," he said to Ohrante. He paid the market-stall proprietor. "You are with the Indians who are camped outside the city, I presume?" he added.

Joseph said they were and thanked him. As for Ohrante, he needed no knowledge of English to tell him what had happened and his anger vanished.

"Please select something for yourself too," the officer said to Joseph. "Perhaps one of these burning glasses . . ."

He took one in his hand, picked up a dry twig from the ground, and showed the two chiefs how the stick could be set afire by letting the bright sun shine on it through the glass.

Joseph's eyes glowed with delight. The officer smiled again. "I am sorry that it is not allowed to take things here in the market without paying for them. But since I am one of General Haldimand's aides I can tell you there will be many presents for all the Six Nations after the council is over."

When he had gone, Ohrante said, "Perhaps it will be best if we take up the war tomahawk for the Red Jackets, Thayendanegea. Have you ever received presents from any of the settlers who have taken the warpath against our great father the King?"

Joseph had to admit that he had not. Pleased as he was with his burning glass, his own thoughts had been much like Ohrante's. Yet he felt strongly his responsibility toward his people. Gratitude for presents must not cause him to make the wrong decision.

The two chiefs spent an hour or more in the market looking at all the fascinating things displayed there—cloth of all the bright colors of the rainbow, hatchets and knives whose edges gleamed with sharpness, scissors, needles, little bells that tinkled, pipes of polished wood, cheap necklaces, and other jewelry aglow with bright-colored stones of glass.

Later that afternoon a messenger from the city delivered a large bundle to Joseph's tent. As the war chief untied it even his natural Indian impassiveness could not keep him from uttering a cry of pleasure.

In the package was a complete new suit of clothing. There were moccasins of the finest soft deerskin, a leather tunic, deerskin kilt, breechcloth, leggings, and shoulder belt of fine cloth, and a leather waist belt. All were ornamented with beads and porcupine quills in bright colors, leather fringe, and panels of colored cloth. There was a blanket, too, of smooth-textured dark blue wool.

Enclosed with the new things was a note from Colonel Johnson, who was staying within the city. "I thought you would like to have these since you will lead all the other chiefs in council tomorrow," it said. "As the war chief of the Six Nations you will want to look your best when you meet Governor Carleton and General Haldimand."

At noon the next day the cannon in the fort on top of Mount Royal thundered out a salute to the Indian visitors, and a few minutes later Colonel Johnson arrived at the camp. Joseph, looking every inch a leader in his new clothes, held himself with a new air of dignity and authority. And the colonel's expression as he surveyed him was praise enough for Joseph.

With Colonel Johnson were Lieutenant Colonel Butler and his son Walter. Joseph did not like the Butlers. John Butler was Colonel Johnson's brother-in-law, and both men were often at

Johnson Hall. The Mohawk distrusted them. In their faces he sometimes detected a look suggesting they could be as cruel and ferocious as the most bloodthirsty warrior.

A long roll of drums sounded from the direction of the city. "They are coming now," Colonel Johnson said. "Let us go to the open part of the plain where the council will sit."

Everyone in the Indian camp was flocking toward the scene of the council, attracted first by the drums and now by the added sound of music from several bands. The entire army of General Haldimand was marching out onto the plain.

In all his experience on the warpath with the English, Joseph had never seen such a display of military might. It seemed as if the scarlet column had no end. There were scores of officers in brilliant uniforms heavy with gold lace.

When at last the vast army halted and grounded its arms, Colonel Johnson touched Joseph's arm. "Here come our hosts," he said.

Joseph saw a magnificent shiny black coach, ornamented in crimson and gold, drawn by four milk-white horses. A band struck up a martial air. An officer raised his sword.

"Pre—sent . . . *arms!*" he shouted and the army brought its muskets up to salute.

The coach drew up and His Excellency Sir Guy Carleton, governor of Canada, and General Sir Frederick Haldimand, commander-in-chief of His Majesty George III's armies in North America, got out. All the cannon on Mount Royal thundered again.

Advancing with Colonel Johnson to meet their hosts, Joseph was introduced to the governor. Sir Guy Carleton wore a suit of crimson satin adorned with white lace and ruffles; on his breast shone a decoration from the King, a bejeweled golden medallion. He was handsome, with an aristocratic face, and although the words he spoke were cordial there was a certain coldness about him.

Joseph felt more liking for General Haldimand, a big man with a high, square forehead. Although the general's expression seemed as stern and hard as a rock, his brown eyes were kindly.

The Indians grouped in a wide circle about them were shouting, "Ho! ho!" Then an officer held up his hand for silence and Sir Guy Carleton began his speech. After he had assured them they were welcome to Montreal, he pointed to the army drawn up on the plain.

"My brothers," he said, "these soldiers are but a small part of the armies of the King your father. I assure you His Majesty will send many more to America, as many as are needed to put down the rebellion in his colonies to the south. He asks you, his children, who are so mighty in battle, so keen-eyed on forest trails, to give him your loyal service in the war."

He spoke then of the long friendship between the English and the Six Nations. "Continue your allegiance to the King," he went on. "Do not break the solemn agreement made by your forefathers, for it will be to your best advantage to continue as allies of His Majesty."

What he meant by the words "to your best advantage" became clearer when General Haldimand got up to make his speech.

"In fighting for the King you will be fighting for your lands and possessions," the general told the chiefs and warriors. "I promise you that whatever you lose of your property during the war His Majesty will make up to you when peace returns."

When General Haldimand sat down there were more speeches by the chiefs of the Six Nations. Joseph listened intently, weighing the sachems' words against what the English leaders had said. His own turn would come last. Was this the time to rouse the warriors to take up the war belt and join the English?

He felt that he could trust General Haldimand's promise. But suppose the Americans were victorious . . . what would happen then?

Joseph wondered, too, whether all the tribes of the Six Nations would take the warpath for the English. He caught a note of unfriendliness in the speeches of the Oneida and Tuscarora chiefs. He thought he could count on the rest, including the powerful Senecas, who could put a thousand braves into battle. But he himself had said to Ohrante that the Indians could be strong only if they were united . . .

When he rose to speak he had reached a decision. This was not the time to pledge his people's support of the English. He contented himself with acknowledging the governor's welcome and pledging the Six Nations not to forget their ancient alliance with Britain.

As the council closed, the treaty of friendship was solemnly renewed with the exchange of wampum strings and belts and the smoking of many pipes. Nothing was said of taking the warpath.

The English leaders were not yet ready to give up, however. True to the promise of General Haldimand's aide in the market place, there was a lavish distribution of presents for all. And the next morning, as the Indians prepared to leave, a messenger came to Joseph's tent and handed him a belt of wampum. With it was a note from Colonel Johnson.

"I am sending wampum belts to you and some of the other chiefs, calling you to sit in council with His Excellency Governor Carleton this afternoon," the letter said. *"A guide will be sent to conduct you to the governor's palace."*

Once again Joseph had a feeling that something important was going to happen. He reread Colonel Johnson's note to see if he had missed any clue in it, but he found nothing.

He was pleased to see Ohrante among the chiefs who went into the city that afternoon. The warriors, in full regalia, walked silently in single file through the gates. At the great stone mansion, which Governor Carleton occupied when he came from the capital at Quebec, they were shown into a large reception hall.

There the governor stood behind an immense, highly polished mahogany table covered with papers and documents. On each side of him were General Haldimand, Colonel Johnson, a number of high-ranking officers of the army, and an interpreter.

Not at all awed by the scene, several of the sachems wandered about, looking at all that was new to them. Three went behind the governor to stare up at the full-length oil paintings of King George and Queen Charlotte hanging on the wall. Another examined the British flag that stood in a standard near the table.

"Brothers," Colonel Johnson reminded them, "Sir Guy Carleton has something to say to you if you will arrange yourselves here in front of the table."

This being done, the governor addressed them. "My brothers," he said, "upon Colonel Johnson's recommendation I have selected you to come here to hear a message from our great King. His Majesty is graciously pleased to invite you, the leaders of his children of the Six Nations, to cross the sea and visit London."

When his words had been translated, the chiefs gazed at each other without speaking. Some of them looked alarmed.

"Brother!" one said at last. "I have heard that the white men's big canoes are sometimes dashed to pieces by monsters and evil spirits that live at the bottom of the great lake between America and England. I do not wish to make such a dangerous journey."

There was a murmur of agreement among the chiefs. Without another word but with fear written on their faces, they turned and left the reception chamber. Only Joseph and Ohrante remained.

Colonel Johnson turned to them. "Our brothers are brave in battle," he said, "but the thought of crossing the ocean seems to dismay them. What is your answer to His Majesty's invitation?"

Joseph looked questioningly at Ohrante. He saw the old light of adventure burning brightly in his friend's eyes.

"We will cross the big lake to the castle of the English called London," he told Governor Carleton.

Chapter 11

Joseph and Ohrante, with Colonel Johnson and Captain Tice, one of the colonel's staff, embarked at Montreal in the ship that was to take them to London. The Mohawk war chief had hoped he might get home before leaving, but there was not time and he had to be content with sending Catherine a message by courier telling her of his extended journey.

Crossing the Atlantic was an awesome experience. They were at sea nearly a month. But at last the ship sailed into a broad estuary, up the River Thames and into the harbor of London, so crowded with ships from every part of the world that their masts looked like the bare trunks of trees in a forest swept by fire.

Even before they landed, the visiting chiefs could see that London was so enormous it made Montreal seem like a small village. In every direction, as far as they could see on both sides of the river, were many buildings crowded close together. Most were of red brick, although a few of the larger ones were of stone.

A Mr. Tompkins from the office of the King's Minister for the Colonies met them at the dock. He seemed a little frightened when he saw the Indians in their native costumes with their tomahawks and scalping knives, but he was very pleasant. They all got into a hackney coach and set off through the city.

The streets were jammed with wagons, carts, and coaches, and what little room was left at the sides was filled with a pushing, jostling crowd of people. The noise was deafening. Above the rumble of the traffic and the drivers' shouts as they cracked their whips they could hear peddlers crying their wares: "Lily-white vinegar!"—"Buy a rat trap, a very fine rat trap!"—"Scissors to grind!" Bells rang everywhere.

The coach had entered the oldest part of London, known as the City. Mr. Tompkins pointed out the gigantic Church of Saint Paul with its vast dome, and other interesting sights.

Arching over the street ahead was a stone gateway. Mr. Tompkins pointed to it.

"That is Temple Bar," he said. "At one time the City was surrounded by a wall with ten gates in it. All but this and one other have been removed now."

Joseph and Ohrante put their heads out of the coach window.

"What is that up there?" Ohrante asked in his native language, pointing to the top of Temple Bar. "It looks like a man's head."

"It does, though I don't think it can be," the Mohawk replied. "I will ask Mr. Tompkins."

"Your friend is right," said Tompkins. "It is the head of a man who was beheaded after leading a rebellion against the King many years ago."

"Beheaded?" Joseph repeated.

"His head was chopped off."

When Joseph had translated this the two chiefs stared at each other. Then, in Mohawk, Joseph said, "It is very hard to understand the English. They call us savages because we scalp our enemies. Yet they chop off the heads of theirs and put them up just as we string scalps at the door of the long house."

Colonel Johnson and Captain Tice were staying with some friends in London, but Joseph and Ohrante were to lodge at an inn. The coach rolled past another enormous church that Mr. Tompkins called Westminster Abbey, turned in at a narrow, shabby street, and went through an arched gateway into a yard where several larger coaches were loading and discharging passengers.

"This is The Swan with Two Necks, where the—ah—savages are to lodge," Mr. Tompkins said rather apologetically to Colonel Johnson. "Westminster's a poor neighborhood, though I believe they'll find the inn quite comfortable."

Colonel Johnson put his head out of the window, looked around, and then turned to Mr. Tompkins with his eyebrows raised. "There must be some mistake," he said. "They'll have to lodge here tonight, I suppose, but I shall speak to the Secretary of State for the Colonies about it when I see him tomorrow."

The two chiefs liked the room they were to share. It looked out over the courtyard, where they could see the big mail coaches arriving from and departing for every part of England. When they were settled, the innkeeper himself, a short, round, red-faced man, came to see if they had everything needed for their comfort. He remained to ask many questions about America and their life there and to answer their questions about London.

"Colonel Johnson seems to think we should have a better place to stay," Joseph observed after the innkeeper had gone, "but I see nothing wrong with this English long house, and the sachem is as friendly and pleasant a man as I have ever met."

When Colonel Johnson returned the next day he said, "There has been a mistake and you are to move to one of the best inns in London. It will be more suitable, especially for you, Joseph, since as the war chief of the Six Nations you rank as a visiting king."

Joseph and Ohrante looked at each other and shook their heads. "If you do not mind, Colonel Johnson," Joseph said, "we should like to stay here."

It was agreed they would remain. That afternoon Colonel Johnson took them on a sight-seeing tour. There seemed to be no end to London. It was like a great, swarming human anthill. Everywhere there were people, thousands of them, rich and poor. The ladies of fashion were dressed in such splendor as to put those of Montreal to shame, and wore hoop skirts so wide that they sometimes had to go through doors sideways. Yet in many of the courts and yards and alleys that went twisting off the larger streets even more people lived in terrible poverty and squalor.

Joseph and Ohrante never tired of roaming the cobbled streets, especially at night, when the shops, with their bow windows and carved fronts, were all lighted with wax tapers.

They grew familiar with the interior of the shops too, for Colonel Johnson saw that they had pocket money to buy the trinkets of which they were so fond. In one of the shops Joseph bought a gold ring and had it inscribed: *"J. Brant—Thayendanegea."*

One thing marred his pleasure. "Our Indian dress makes people stare at us," he told Colonel Johnson. "I did not mind it at first, but now I feel like one of those wild beasts we saw exhibited in cages when we went to the great fort called the Tower of London."

"I will take you and Ohrante to a tailor," said the colonel. "He will make English suits for you so that you will not attract so much attention."

A few days later both braves were as elegantly dressed as any young Englishman of fashion. Joseph chose a dark blue broadcloth coat and breeches and an embroidered yellow satin waistcoat. Ohrante, whose taste ran to brighter colors, selected a scarlet coat, bright blue breeches, and white waistcoat.

Both chiefs were delighted. In fact, the day the new clothes were delivered to The Swan with Two Necks, Ohrante did not want to take his off at all and would have worn them to bed if Joseph had not told him it would spoil them.

Time passed quickly, for there were always new things to do and new sights to see. For Joseph, as the leading chief of the Six Nations, there was also a rather tiresome round of calls upon government officials with Colonel Johnson. Among them was Lord George Germain, Secretary of State for the Colonies, to whom he spoke of his people's fear of losing their lands. Like Governor Carleton and General Haldimand, Germain assured the war chief that the Indians would be treated fairly.

The days lengthened into weeks until one day in April, Joseph said to Ohrante, "We have been here so long that sometimes I forget I am an Indian."

Ohrante surveyed himself in the large mirror their friend the innkeeper had placed in their room. He looked a little wistful. "Sometimes I wish I could see my village again and go out in the forest and hunt. It will soon be warm enough to swim in the Onondaga River too. And I miss my wife and children."

"I have been thinking of such things myself, Ohrante. I will ask Colonel Johnson when we are to return to America."

Johnson told Joseph he would not be able to leave for some time. "I must remain to discuss a number of important things in council with the sachems of the King's government, but I will arrange for you and Ohrante to sail soon with Captain Tice. However, there are several things you must do before that."

"What do you wish me to do, Colonel Johnson?"

"Mr. James Boswell has asked for an interview so he can write an article about you for *The London Magazine*. He is a well-known writer. And one of the greatest artists in Europe, Mr. George Romney, has asked to paint a picture of you. Most important of all, you are to have an audience with His Majesty the King."

"Will Ohrante do these things too?" Joseph asked.

"No, it is you these famous people are interested in because you are the war chief of the Six Nations. Meanwhile we will see that Ohrante is kept amused."

The war chief was somewhat disappointed when he met James Boswell at the Turk's Head Tavern in Soho, where the writer invited him for supper. He had expected an older man in elegant clothes; instead, Boswell was soberly dressed in a dark suit that showed signs of wear, and he was about Joseph's own age. He seemed a little pompous, as if he considered the Mohawk far beneath him.

But once Boswell began to ask questions, Joseph forgot all that. Many of the white men he had met seemed to want to talk only about themselves. But James Boswell listened intently, as if the Indian's words were the most interesting he had ever heard.

Joseph found himself telling Boswell all about his life in the Upper Castle of the Mohawks, of Catherine and the children, of the house he had built for Owaisa, how the fur trade with the English was carried on, and his adventures on the warpath.

"I was surprised to see you wearing English dress," Boswell remarked, and when Joseph told him the reason he said, "I had hoped to see you in your native costume—especially to see the hatchet I am told Indians carry—the tomahawk, do you call it?"

For reply Joseph reached under his coat and drew from his belt his cherished combination pipe and tomahawk with his name engraved on an inlaid silver plate. He did it so quickly that the writer leaped back from the table in alarm, almost upsetting his chair.

Then he smiled and sat down again. "For a moment I fancied you were going to show me how it is used," he said. "But why do you carry it in London?"

"I have heard," Joseph replied, "that there is a tribe of savage white men in London who lie in ambush to rob people and sometimes kill them."

James Boswell threw back his head and laughed. "You are right!" he exclaimed. "We call them Mohawks—or Mohocks, as most people say—because your tribe is known in London as very ferocious. That is why I pictured you as a savage-looking man instead of one whose appearance, voice, and manners are those of a fine gentleman."

Boswell had many other questions. Because he liked the famous writer, Joseph answered them all as fully as possible. He found sitting for his portrait by George Romney a less enjoyable experience, however.

At the artist's fine mansion in Cavendish Square a servant showed him into a great room cluttered with easels containing many paintings, some finished, some only partly done. Then Romney, a handsome man with a long, rather sharp nose and a high forehead, came in. He stared irritably at Joseph.

"Why do you come here like this?" he snapped. "Do you expect me to paint you in English dress? I was told I was to paint a savage. Go away and come back tomorrow dressed like one."

When Joseph reappeared the next morning in full chief's regalia, Romney nodded curtly and put him in a chair near an immense window which lighted the studio. Then he began to sketch the outlines of Joseph's head and body on a canvas. He would make a few strokes and then stand with his head on one side, staring at his subject with narrowed eyes. He never spoke except to bark, "Raise your head a bit!"—"Look straight at me, now!"—"Sit still! How can I work if you don't sit still?"

At last the painter said, "Come back at the same time tomorrow."

Romney covered the picture each day as soon as he had finished his work, so that Joseph could not see it. But at last one morning he laid down his brush and palette.

"Come and look," he said.

As he stood before the easel, Joseph's mouth fell open in amazement. After what Romney had said about painting a savage, the Mohawk had half expected to see himself pictured in the act of scalping an enemy. Instead a dignified and kindly man in savage dress looked out at him from the picture.

"It is very fine," he said. "Can you send it to me at The Swan with Two Necks?"

Now it was Romney's jaw that fell open. "Send it!" he shouted. "My work! Are you insane?"

It had not occurred to the crestfallen Mohawk until then that the picture was not for him. Perhaps Romney saw that it was quite natural he should have thought so. The artist's manner became kinder and he took pains to explain that it was an honor to have his portrait painted for a famous nobleman, the Earl of Warwick, who had ordered it and would pay a great deal of money for it.

Joseph went back to the inn thinking wistfully how much he would have liked to show it to Catherine, his mother, Molly, and his brother warriors. But he never saw the picture again after he left England, although today it hangs in the National Gallery in Ottawa, the capital of Canada.

There remained only Joseph's audience with the King before he sailed for New York. He was thinking about it one afternoon when he and Ohrante, after shopping for presents for their wives and children, went into the Church of Saint Paul and climbed the long flight of steps leading to the vast dome. Joseph, who had been unusually quiet since they had left the inn, gazed out over the city.

"Something is troubling you," Ohrante said. "I have noticed it for several days. What is it, my brother?"

"I have been thinking of what I will say to our great father the King, Ohrante. He will want to know whether our people will fight for him, I am sure."

"Have you decided what to say, Thayendanegea?"

"It is hard to decide," Joseph replied. "Before we went to Montreal I told you I thought if all the Indian Nations in America could unite, the red men would be strong enough to obtain fair treatment from the whites. Since that seems impossible now, I believe the Hodenosaunee must fight to save their homes and lands. If we do not, the new settlers who come after the war will drive us out."

"But the settlers will come whether we fight or not."

"We can demand protection for our lands as a price for fighting in the war. The English have already promised it. But unless we take the warpath for the victors we will surely be driven away."

"How can we tell who will win?"

Joseph's pointing finger swept the horizon. "This village of the English is so big that our brothers at home will be sure we are boasting when we tell them of it. You have seen the wild pigeons darken the sun as they fly north in the spring, Ohrante. Yet I do not believe all of them would be enough to make a dinner for every person in London. The settlers in America can never win against such a mighty nation as England!"

The long-awaited day of Joseph's meeting with the King arrived at last. Colonel Johnson and he, accompanied by Lord George Germain, were driven in Germain's huge gilded coach, attended by liveried coachmen and footmen, to St. James's Palace.

The palace was a red brick building with two turreted towers, and although it was located in the heart of London it fronted on a beautiful park with green lawns and many trees. They were ushered up a grand staircase and into an anteroom. A few minutes later an inner door opened and the King's secretary appeared.

"His Majesty will see you and the other gentlemen now, my lord," he said to Germain and showed them into the Presence

Chamber, a magnificent room hung with tapestries and oil paintings. At the opposite end of the room was a massive chair upholstered in red; over it extended a red satin canopy with the royal arms emblazoned in silver. There sat a man, not much older than Joseph, in a robe of crimson velvet and ermine.

In his awe the war chief almost forgot the instructions he had received, but seeing Lord Germain and Colonel Johnson kneeling, he quickly dropped to his knees.

The King, with a motion of his hand, bade his visitors arise.

"I have the honor," Lord Germain said, "to present in audience with Your Gracious Majesty, Guy Johnson, superintendent of Indian affairs in Your Majesty's royal province of New York, and Joseph Brant of the Mohawk tribe of Indians in New York, chieftain of the Confederacy of the Six Nations."

Joseph found himself returning His Majesty's curious gaze. A vague feeling of disappointment struck him. The King looked like any other white man! He was quite handsome, of fair complexion, but a little stout, and his blue eyes were rather prominent. Somehow Joseph had expected him to resemble a god, although he had no idea of what a god looked like. And where were the Crown Jewels? He had pictured the King as covered with them from head to foot. While his robe was gorgeous he wore no crown and held neither jeweled sword nor scepter.

Then he remembered what Colonel Johnson had told him: "King George is a very simple man. Much of his time is spent in his palace at Windsor, outside of London. His Majesty likes to work on his farm there. The people often call him 'Farmer George.'"

Again Joseph marveled at this strange race whose mighty King himself did not scorn to work in the fields like a squaw!

Colonel Johnson addressed the King. "Your servant, Joseph Brant, has come from America, Your Majesty, to speak for his people. He humbly asks that Your Royal Highness hear his words."

"We are gratified that our worthy Joseph Brant has come to England, Colonel Johnson," the King replied. He turned to Joseph. "We welcome you to England and trust that your stay has been pleasant. When you return to America, assure our beloved children of the Six Nations of our love and concern for them."

The King paused. Joseph's great moment had come. He drew himself up to his full height and looked straight at George III.

"Your Majesty," he said, "I have come with my people's pledge of love and devotion to you, their father. My people trust that you will always treat them with fairness and that you will permit them always to stay on the lands where their ancestors lived long before the white men crossed the sea to America."

He drew a long breath. "My people are only a few of the children of Your Majesty in England and your colonies, but they are mighty in battle. They will show that they are grateful to their great father. I will lead my warriors on the warpath against the settlers who have rebelled against you, Your Majesty!"

Chapter 12

As he came to the end of his war speech at Oswego, Joseph paused, looking at the warriors gathered around the council fire. Although their impassive faces held no sign of their feelings, he knew with the instinct of a leader that they were ready now. This was the moment . . .

For an instant he hesitated, his thoughts leaping back to the journeys he had made, to the councils with the chiefs in their villages since he and Ohrante had returned from England. More than once he had been discouraged. Even now he seemed to see the stony faces of the sachems as he tried to make them see that the wisest course of the Six Nations was to fight for the English.

Ohrante had told him what the trouble was when he visited the Onondagas' castle. "They trust you, Thayendanegea," he had said, "but they are not sure of the promises of the English that we shall keep our lands after the war. They are not even sure the English will win, my brother."

Yet Joseph had thought he had convinced them, even in the principal castle of the Senecas at Kanadesaga, where he had faced the opposition of his implacable enemy, Red Jacket. In full confidence he had summoned the war council here at Oswego, where Colonel St. Leger's British force lay poised to stroke through the Mohawk Valley toward Albany. There it would meet General Burgoyne's powerful army, sweeping down from Canada, and General Howe's, thrusting up Hudson's River from New York City.

Yesterday Joseph's confidence had been staggered. In their speeches, the Oneida and Onondaga chiefs had urged the Six Nations not to fight. Afterward their warriors had silently dissolved into the forest to the east . . . Could Red Jacket, unable to convince his own braves, have used the magic of his slippery tongue on the other two Nations?

The Oneidas and Onondagas had gone—no, not all of the Onondagas. His loyal, devoted friend Ohrante had prevented that. That night, as Joseph lay stretched before his campfire, plunged into despair, Ohrante had slipped out of the darkness with a catlike tread and had thrown himself down beside his friend, who had not seen him since afternoon.

"When our warriors went with Chief Kaghswughtioni into the forest, I followed and talked to as many as I could," he had said in a low tone. "I have brought back a small band who will remain to fight with the British."

Now, at the crucial point of his war speech, Joseph reflected that he would not soon forget what Ohrante had done.

In this moment he must decide. Should he lead the remaining tribes on the warpath for the English? Time and time again he had said, "It is only by uniting that the Indians can be strong." Now the Six Nations were divided.

He thought of what he had promised the King. "I will lead my warriors on the warpath against the settlers who have rebelled against you, Your Majesty."

Joseph Brant took up the huge war belt of white and purple wampum and held it high above his head for all to see. Then he hurled it to the ground. With a shrill whoop a Seneca chief snatched it up. There rose a great shout from the circle of men.

The war dance began . . .

The next morning an Indian runner slithered out of the forest bearing a letter for Joseph. When he had read it he took it to Sir John Johnson, who was commanding the Royal Greens, his regiment of settlers loyal to the King.

"My sister Molly has sent a message from Mount Johnson," the war chief said. "The rebel leader Nicholas Herkimer is marching with eight hundred men to Fort Stanwix on the upper waters of the Mohawk River."

The baronet's eyes narrowed. "We must act quickly," he said. "I will inform Colonel St. Leger at once."

That afternoon Joseph was called to headquarters and introduced to St. Leger, whose force had arrived from Montreal only the day before. The British commander was a handsome officer with features so delicate that he looked almost girlish.

"It is a pleasure to meet you, for Governor Carleton has spoken well of you," St. Leger said, then smiled and added, "—Captain Brant."

Joseph stared. He thought he must have misunderstood but Sir John, also smiling, said, "His Majesty the King has been graciously pleased to grant you a commission as a captain in the British Army, Joseph."

Overwhelmed by the honor that had come to him, the war chief was at a loss for words, but Colonel St. Leger hurried on to another subject. His finger traced a route on a map spread out before him. "We will go up the Oswego River," he said. "Before Herkimer reaches Fort Stanwix we will intercept him and destroy his army. Have your warriors ready to march at daybreak tomorrow, Captain Brant."

In the ambush on the thickly wooded western rim of a deep ravine, Joseph could look down the Valley where the Mohawk River turned and twisted. The Indians called the region Ohiska or the Place of Nettles; the whites knew it as Oriskany.

Crouched in the underbrush with Ohrante and the other chiefs, the Mohawk waited tensely. His warriors, though invisible, lay all about him. Behind them, in the forest, was a detachment of Royal Greens and Rangers sent out under Colonel John Butler from the camp where St. Leger was besieging Fort Stanwix.

Naked save for his breechcloth and moccasins, his face streaked with war paint and his scalp lock bristling with bear's grease, Joseph wished he might have worn the scarlet uniform of his new rank, but he knew how foolhardy it would have been in an ambush.

He stiffened as Ohrante's hand gripped his arm. Then he peered into the distance, his eyes black slits. Ah! He saw it too. Something was moving along the hillside a mile away . . . a white horse!

"Wait till the head of the rebel force has crossed the ravine," he whispered to his chiefs. "Then send the warriors down there and cut the column in half!"

The chiefs vanished into the brush. A few minutes later Joseph recognized Herkimer's stocky, black-haired figure on the white horse. He knew the American leader well. Herkimer's house stood not far from the one he had built for Owaisa. The Mohawk liked and respected his neighbor, who always treated the Indians fairly. Now Herkimer was his enemy.

The men in the long American column had no uniforms. They were mostly Dutch and German settlers of the Valley, who had never liked the English rule.

Herkimer crossed the bottom of the ravine and urged his horse up the other side. As he reached the top he passed so close to Joseph that it seemed as if his keen dark eyes were looking straight at the concealed war chief. But the American rode on.

Then it came: flame, smoke, and an echoing crash of gunfire from every part of the ravine's rim, followed by the frightful war whoop. As Joseph leaped down the slope the startled center of Herkimer's column crumpled to pieces before his eyes.

Some ran this way, some that, in a panic-stricken rush for cover. Shadowy bronze figures skulked from tree to tree, pouring a murderous fire on the trapped Americans. The ground was already strewn with dead and dying men, while others were in wild flight. The Indians had surrounded the rear of the column, cutting it to pieces, overturning the wagons of Herkimer's supply train, and shooting the horses.

Satisfied with the progress of the battle in the ravine, Joseph swung back up the slope. At the top both the Indians and Butler's men were attacking the head of Herkimer's column.

The Americans were trying to fight their way back to the aid of their comrades in the rear. Just then, in an open glade in the forest, Joseph saw Herkimer riding toward him. With Ohrante at his side he took cover.

As Herkimer galloped forward his horse suddenly reared, gave a shrill scream, and fell dead. The American leader, thrown clear, was on his feet in an instant.

Flame belched from Ohrante's musket. Herkimer staggered and fell but again he got up. He unstrapped the saddle from the dead horse, limped with it to a beech tree not ten yards from the two chiefs, threw it down, and sat on it.

Joseph saw a spreading red stain on the American's thigh. One of Herkimer's men crawled out of the brush and came up to him. "Let me help you back into the woods where it is safe, General," he said.

Calmly, though his face was contorted with pain, Herkimer filled a pipe, put a wad of tow and a little powder in the pan of his musket, pulled the trigger, and applied the lighted tow to the tobacco.

"I will face the enemy," he said.

At Joseph's side Ohrante raised his reloaded gun. The war chief put out his hand and thrust up the muzzle.

"No!" he whispered to his friend. "This is a brave man!"

For an instant Ohrante looked surprised. Then he nodded and lowered the musket. Joseph motioned with his head and the two warriors silently crept back into the forest, where Butler's men were advancing toward the enemy.

The war chief had seen an expression in the Onondaga's eyes that made his heart surge with gladness. He had a feeling that Ohrante too was beginning to understand that there were times when the white man's mercy was best.

From that moment it was as though Herkimer's courage had inspired his men to do the impossible. From his post under the beech tree the American general calmly directed them, forming the troops to resist the assault by Colonel Butler's force. A sudden thunderstorm, coming up from nowhere, caused a lull in the battle. When it slackened, the Americans charged with fixed bayonets, yelling wildly as the Royal Greens and Rangers closed in on them. Joseph saw the English line buckle and fall back in disorder. Then, in stricken astonishment, he heard the Indians' cry of retreat: "Oonah! Oonah!"

The violence of the unexpected charge threw Royal Greens, Rangers, and warriors into headlong flight. Butler's force might have been annihilated but for the arrival of a fresh detachment from St. Leger's camp. But it had to retreat. And although Nicholas Herkimer would die a few days later from his wound, he had gained something as good as a victory: he had stopped St. Leger's march to Albany.

In camp that night Joseph Brant lay wakeful for a long time. He was still stunned by the fury with which Herkimer's force, cut apart, demoralized, and beaten, had rallied to drive the English back. Could it be that he had been mistaken in thinking the King's armies were invincible? He thought of the villages of the Six Nations, of his people who loved the green forests, sparkling streams and lakes of the beautiful country where they had lived long before the white man came. What would happen to them if the Americans should win the war . . . ?

Chapter 13

After the battle most of the Indians returned to their villages for the winter; but Joseph went to Fort Niagara, where Colonel Guy Johnson and Sir John, accompanied by their families, had established headquarters for the regiments of settlers who were loyal to the Crown. The Mohawk Valley, held by the Americans as a result of St. Leger's failure at Oriskany, was hostile to the Johnsons. Because of her connection with them, Molly Johnson felt it was best to leave Mount Johnson. She came to Niagara, bringing Joseph's wife and children, who had been staying with her.

While the war chief was overjoyed to have them with him, and the family shared comfortable quarters in the fort, it was not like home. He spoke of the future one fall day when he and Catherine had strolled out on the ramparts.

"When the war is over I will build a house in the valley of the Yenonanatche," he told her, using the Indian name for the Mohawk River. "Then we will settle there in peace, I hope, for the rest of our lives."

Catherine's face was anxious as she looked up at her husband. "I hope so too, Thayendanegea. You have been away so much since we were married. Do you think the war will be over soon?"

For a moment Joseph gazed out over the lake. Then, not wanting to worry her, he assumed a confident tone. "When spring comes the King will send more armies to America. They will drive the Americans from our Valley and destroy them wherever they are foolish enough to fight."

In his heart he was not so sure. News had already reached Fort Niagara that the British General Burgoyne's mighty army had been defeated in a battle at Saratoga and forced to surrender. But surely, the war chief thought, as he had told Catherine, in the spring . . .

In the spring no new British Army came to reinforce the Johnsons at Niagara, however. They were anxious to regain control of the Mohawk Valley, but their loyalist regiments were not strong enough to take the American-held forts there. For the time being they had to be content with making raids on unfortified villages in the surrounding country.

Leaving his family at Fort Niagara, Joseph journeyed east, rounding up his warriors. He led them into the country south of the Mohawk and established headquarters at the Indian village of Ouaquaga. From there they struck with savage ferocity at American settlements in the region.

At five o'clock on a summer morning the settlement of Springfield at the head of Otsego Lake lay asleep, its dwellings silent and peaceful. A quarter of an hour later they were aflame, flaring torches in the ghostly dawn, the peace of the village shattered by the shrill frightfulness of the war whoop, the roar of gunfire, the crackling of the flames, and the screams of women and children. The half-naked figures of Joseph Brant's warriors flitted about in the glare.

Crouched in the shadow of a barn, the war chief peered quickly around its corner, then jerked his head back as a settler's musket ball, missing him by inches, sent up a shower of splinters. Then he leaned out again, took aim, and fired. The white man fell.

Someone touched Joseph's shoulder. He turned to see Chief Little Aaron. In his left hand the sachem held his musket, in the right a bloody tomahawk. Scalps dangled from his belt.

"Most of the white men who are still alive have fled," he reported. "Our warriors are searching for any who may be hiding. The women and children have been taken to the village square as you ordered, Thayendanegea."

"That is well," Joseph replied. "We will go there now."

In the square the terrified captives stood huddled, watched by several braves. A guard, grotesquely painted, one eye circled in red and the other in black, advanced toward the war chief.

"We have obeyed your command, Thayendanegea," he said, "though we do not understand why it was necessary to wait till now to kill these white squaws and papooses."

Joseph looked him in the eye. "Let them go, Tiahogwando," he said.

The brave scowled. "They are our captives. Why should we let them go?"

The war chief pointed to the other Indian's belt. "You have many scalps already, Tiahogwando. If you want more, join those who are chasing the fleeing white warriors. The white squaws and little ones are to be released."

There were mutterings from some of the other guards. For a moment Tiahogwando's sullen eyes clashed with Joseph's steady gaze. Then they wavered. The warrior motioned with his head to his companions. In single file they followed him out of the square.

Late in October a light snow had fallen over the wilderness. Now, in early November, patches of it still remained in the hollows of the bleak hills. Making their way north, Joseph Brant's five hundred warriors avoided these places in order to leave no trace of their passing. They moved on padded feet; no twig snapped under the brown leaves to warn a lurking enemy scout of their presence.

Joseph, a commanding figure in his blue broadcloth tunic and kilt, a blue blanket with a bright red border over his shoulders, was at the head of the single file of braves. As he reached the top of a high ridge one of his scouts glided out of the woods.

"Men, Thayendanegea!" he grunted, pointing toward the Valley below. "Many men, some white, some maybe white, maybe red."

The warriors had seen the scout's gesture and were taking cover. Joseph crouched behind a rock and scanned the Valley intently.

He turned to Ohrante, who lay close by. "The man leading the others on horseback looks like Colonel Butler's son. Do you think it is, my brother?"

"I think so," Ohrante replied. He stared down into the Valley, craning his neck. "Yes, I am sure of it now."

Joseph did not look happy. Now he knew why his scout had not been sure whether all of Captain Walter Butler's men were white: many of the Rangers dressed like warriors. The settlers called them "blue-eyed Indians"—cruel, inhuman men who scalped and tortured their enemies. That summer, Colonel John Butler, leading them on a raid in the Wyoming Valley, had allowed them to kill and scalp white men, women, and children without mercy. Walter Butler was known to be no less ruthless than his father; and he was contemptuous of Indians.

Joseph had an impulse to turn back and evade the encounter but it was too late. Captain Butler's arm was already raised in greeting even though the Indians were hidden from his view. His own scouts must have reported their approach.

A smile flickered on Butler's thin lips as he reached the top of the ridge, but it held no friendliness.

"Ah, *Captain* Brant," he said. Looking down from his saddle, he gave Joseph a mocking salute. "I had hoped to meet you on this trail since I knew you were somewhere in the vicinity. Where are you going?"

"To Fort Niagara," the war chief replied. "We will go into winter quarters there."

"Not so fast, Captain." Butler drew a paper from his pocket. "I have orders here from Sir John Johnson placing me in command of this detachment of two hundred of my father's Rangers"—the sneering smile played again on his lips—"and of you and your Indians. We are going to raid Cherry Valley, or Karatonga, as you call it. You will go with us, Captain."

Joseph bristled. With a scarcely perceptible movement he let his blanket slide off his shoulders a little so that his captain's silver epaulets were exposed. He was proud of his rank in His Majesty's army and he did not like the tone in which the white man spoke, as though he considered Joseph his inferior.

"It is very late in the season," he told Butler. "My warriors want to reach Fort Niagara before the big snows come."

Butler smiled coldly. "Surely you are not afraid of the soldiers you *thought* you saw at Cherry Valley——"

Joseph scowled, sensing the note of contempt in Butler's voice. "I do not know what you mean, Captain Butler."

"Last summer you had planned to raid Cherry Valley, Captain, but you were frightened away when you thought you saw troops parading on the green in front of the stockade."

Joseph's scowl deepened. "I was not frightened," he said in a cold, level tone, "but the soldiers were there. I saw them in the distance from a hill in back of the village. I decided I did not have enough warriors to assault the stockade."

Butler sneered again. "You and your warriors were observed as you went away, Captain. It has made the rebels in Cherry Valley laugh at you. The troops you thought you saw were a company of small boys playing at soldiers. Their guns were of wood and their hats of paper!"

Butler's face betrayed his enjoyment of the war chief's discomfiture. "I hope," he continued, "your warriors will never hear of your mistake. Fancy their scorn if they knew their great war chief had been driven away by some little boys! But since I am sure you will obey Sir John's orders and go with us, I will keep your secret."

Joseph could no longer meet Butler's triumphant gaze. The white man was waiting for an answer and at last the war chief said reluctantly, "We will go with you to Karatonga, Captain Butler."

With the craft of weasels, Joseph's Indians and Walter Butler's Rangers crept down the slope of a wooded hill above the village of Cherry Valley. It had snowed during the night, and now, in the dawn, the war chief's blanket became soggy as a cold drizzle fell from the leaden skies.

Down below, along Cherry Valley Creek, he could see the clustered houses of the village. Already the smoke of breakfast fires was curling up from some of the chimneys. The war chief's eyes shifted a little to the left, taking in a crude log fort that had not been there when he had last seen Cherry Valley. His scouts had reported that there were soldiers there now, all right—real ones this time.

All the instincts of humanity that his association with the white men's civilization had brought out in Joseph rebelled at the thought of this raid. Walter Butler was in command of it, and he had taken pains to let the Indians see that, and they knew too that he would not try to curb their savagery.

Something was moving in the dooryard of a house close to the foot of the hill. Joseph's narrowed eyes made out figures in blue uniforms trimmed with red. A guard of some kind . . . the house must be the headquarters of the commanding officer of the fort.

Captain Butler, riding up from the rear where his Rangers were, saw the soldiers too. He nodded to Joseph. The war chief stood up, raised his tomahawk, and gave the war whoop. He heard its shrill echo from five hundred throats as he plunged down the hill. Below him the guard scurried into the house.

Its bolted door went down with a splintering crash before the rush of the Indians. Three of Joseph's braves burst in ahead of him. In the front room of the house the guard met them with a blast of gunfire. Two warriors fell but others overpowered the soldiers and killed them. An officer wearing a colonel's insignia raised a pistol and fired. Joseph heard the ball whine past his ear. Then the colonel fled toward the rear.

The war chief leaped after him, but when he reached the kitchen the American had vanished. A woman cowered there, white-faced with terror. Her frantic eyes met Joseph's in a mute appeal. A Seneca shouldered past him and his death blow silenced the scream in her throat.

The outside door of the kitchen opened and the woman's husband rushed in. His agonized gaze fell on her body and he leaped for his musket over the fireplace. Before he could reach it an Indian snatched it away. Then the white man fell on his knees in prayer.

Joseph Brant felt his scalp lock creep. He wanted to save this man who was praying to the Christian God he himself had accepted. But a Ranger, his head shaved save for a blond scalp lock, his face smeared with war paint, leaped forward and tomahawked the kneeling settler.

Sick at heart, Joseph left the house. As he reached the dooryard the American colonel burst through a door in an ell at the back of the dwelling. Seeing Joseph, he fired his pistol point-blank at him but the bullet went wide. Then the war chief raised his musket. He did not miss . . .

His Indians were everywhere. From houses all over the village yells of triumph mingled with the screams of dying settlers. All around him houses were bursting into flames.

Joseph headed for the fort. He saw puffs of smoke and flame blossoming out from the gunports in its sides. Most of the Rangers were there, deployed and advancing toward it, firing as they went.

The war chief was passing a house that so far was untouched. Acting on impulse, he went into the yard and tried the kitchen door. It was not latched. There in the kitchen an old lady sat by the fire reading a Bible. She looked up placidly as her Indian visitor came in.

"You had better run to the woods, mother," Joseph told her. "The warriors will kill you if they find you here."

The old lady smiled. It was as though Joseph might have been her son. The smile said that in her mother's wisdom she knew best.

"I am not afraid," she said calmly. "Joseph Brant will save me. He does not let his savages kill women and children."

Gazing at her, the war chief thought of his own mother. "I am Joseph Brant," he said gently. "I am not in command and I do not know whether I can save you, but I will try."

He stepped to the window and looked out. Seeing that a party of Senecas was approaching, Joseph glanced quickly about him.

Through an open door in the kitchen he noticed the bedchamber beyond.

"Quick! Get into bed!" he ordered, and she moved to obey him.

Going to the kitchen fireplace, he picked up a charred stick. Then he leaned over the bed in the other room and drew a design on her forehead:

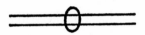

It was the mark he sometimes used to stand for his Indian name: Thayendanegea: "Two Sticks-of-Wood-Bound-Together."

"Show the warriors that mark, mother," he said, "and they will not harm you."

Then he left the house.

From then on Joseph did all he could to see that the lives of as many women and children as possible were spared, no longer caring what Walter Butler thought about it. And although his warriors did not like it, they obeyed their chief.

Meanwhile Butler was leading continued assaults on the fort. Each time a hail of musket balls and cannon fire drove the Rangers back, and at last their losses forced them to give up the attempt.

Huddled together, shivering, threatened with death if they lagged behind, the women and children who had been spared were driven along as Butler's straggling column retired down the Valley.

Ohrante, swaggering along with a dozen scalps at his belt, came up to Joseph.

"I have been looking for you, Thayendanegea," he said. "You must be very happy. At last we have avenged our brothers who fell at Ohiska—though the rebel officer Campbell who led the army against us after I shot Herkimer still lives, I am afraid. He was not at home when some of us went to his house here in this village."

The Mohawk made no reply. He felt no resentment at his friend's jubilation, only a great compassion. Ohrante, who had seen more of the white men's way of life than any of the other chiefs and warriors except himself, still had his savage instincts. It made Joseph realize as never before how difficult was the task of bringing to his people some of the benefits of civilization.

He turned and looked back at the still-smoldering remains of the village. What would happen when the news of Cherry Valley reached the other settlements? Joseph had done what he could, but it would not be enough. It would make no difference to the settlers that Walter Butler, not he, had commanded this merciless raid.

When the warriors had chosen him their war chief, he had promised that if the Six Nations took the warpath he would never lay down the war tomahawk until the name of Thayendanegea was more feared than a thunderbolt. In his raids on Springfield, German Flats, and other villages, he had already made good his boast. But in the future Joseph Brant was to have another sort of fame. In the settlements mothers, warning their children not to stray too far from home in their play, would say, "Do you want Thayendanegea to get you?"

Chapter 14

The winter months that followed the raid on Cherry Valley were hard ones for Joseph Brant. Gazing out over the dreary, snowbound wilderness one afternoon as he trudged along the narrow, hard-packed trail that led to Fort Niagara, he wondered if his whole life was to be filled with bitterness and tragedy. With Catherine following close behind, he was returning from the burial of his mother.

Overwhelmed by his grief, he halted, his head bowed. He felt his wife's hand on his.

"She is better off, my husband," Catherine said gently. "She was old and tired . . ."

"It is my fault!" Joseph burst out. "If I had not gone with Captain Butler to raid Karatonga, the settlers would not have taken vengeance by driving the Mohawks from their castles. She would not have had to make the long journey through the forest with the other squaws and the old men and children to join the warriors here."

He made an agonized gesture toward the wretched huts the Mohawks had built to shelter themselves until spring, when they could decide whether to remain camped outside the fort or go elsewhere. "She would not have had to spend the winter in such a place as this!"

"You did all you could, Thayendanegea," Catherine consoled him. "We wanted your mother and Carrihogo to share our quarters in the fort. It was not your fault that they refused because they were old and did not understand the white men's ways of living. You made sure they had wood for their fire and enough to eat—and even though Sir John Johnson has given the people all that can be spared of the fort's provisions, there is famine in the village, you know."

Joseph did not reply. He was thinking that in the long winter nights the hottest fire could not keep out cold whose grip was as vicious as a bear trap's. At last it had proved too much for his mother, weakened by age and years of toiling and raising children.

Wearily he plodded on toward the fort. Behind him Catherine's voice came again "Do not despair, Thayendanegea. There is much happiness ahead for us yet."

The war chief turned and faced her again. "I do not despair," he said. "It is just that so many things have not turned out as I had hoped. The war—if the English should not win now that the settlers have driven the Mohawks from their castles, we may never be able to go back to the Valley . . . And I am worried about Isaac. He is making too many friends among the Rangers. They are older than he is and they are evil men, Catherine."

He saw distress in her eyes. Not only had Isaac never grown to love his father but as he became older a dislike of Catherine too was showing itself in spite and meanness.

Joseph turned and went on. After all, he reflected, with a wife like Catherine he could never despair. Soon it would be spring. Perhaps it would bring happier days . . .

But the Cherry Valley massacre was to bring even more serious trouble, not only to the Mohawks but to all the tribes of the Six Nations except the neutral Oneidas. The terrified settlers of the entire region demanded that an overwhelming blow be struck at the Indians.

Joseph's first intimation of what was afoot came at Ouaquaga, where he and his warriors had gone in the spring. Ohrante had returned to the Onondagas' country, hoping to get more braves to join him. To the war chief's surprise his friend reached Ouaquaga one morning in June with a large war party.

Ohrante's face was grim as the two chiefs met. "A terrible thing has happened, Thayendanegea!" he cried. "The rebel Colonel Van Schaick marched with five hundred soldiers against our villages and destroyed them!"

"What of your people—are they safe?"

"They escaped into the forest." Ohrante flung out his hands in a despairing gesture. "But everything is gone—the long houses

and crops all burned! I left my wife and children in a rude
shelter I built for them."

"How could this happen when, except for the few braves you
have led, the Onondagas have remained on friendly terms with
the Americans?"

Ohrante folded his arms and stood with his head bowed.
"Many of my brothers have never liked the rebels, even though
they did not take the warpath against them. There have been
a few raids on settlers' houses . . . I warned my brothers it was
bad for their mouths to talk peace while they held the tomahawk behind their backs."

The Onondaga wanted Joseph's warriors to join him at once
against Colonel Van Schaick at Fort Stanwix, now called Fort
Schuyler by the Americans. But while plans for an attack were
being made, a breathless Indian messenger from Fort Niagara
burst into the camp one morning with a dispatch from Sir
John Johnson.

*"The war chief of the Americans, General Washington, is
sending a big army under General Sullivan up the Susquehanna River,"* Sir John had written. *"Another army, commanded by General Clinton, is to go up the Mohawk and join
Sullivan where the Tioga and Susquehanna rivers meet. They
plan to destroy all the villages of the Mohawks, Tuscaroras,
Cayugas, and Senecas. Colonel Butler will march in a few
days and meet you at Chemung on the Tioga."*

Joseph's face reflected grave concern. "We must march at
once," he said to Ohrante. "Unless this American army is
stopped, it may mean the end of the Hodenosaunee. It is not
just our lives and those of our warriors that will be in danger.
This time we must fight to save our homes, our families, and
our Nation."

From the crest of the high ridge Joseph looked down into
the valley of the Tioga. Ohrante was at his side and all along

the ridge his warriors lay waiting. Below, on the broad flats through which the river flowed in a sweeping curve, was another, lower ridge. On it, behind a breastwork concealed under boughs of scrub oak they had cut, were Colonel Butler's Royal Greens, Rangers, some British regulars, and a few of the Indians.

The war chief's gaze shifted down the valley. Suddenly he stiffened. "Look!" he said to Ohrante. "There they come!"

What he saw filled him with dismay. Into the distance, as far as his eyes could see, stretched a double column of soldiers in blue uniforms trimmed with red or white. This combined army of the American Generals Sullivan and Clinton was even larger than he had expected. In its center the sun glinted on the shiny brass of cannon.

"Colonel Butler is sending out skirmishers," said Joseph, pointing to a party of Rangers and Indians sallying forth from the lower ridge, firing as they went. In reply, little puffs of blue smoke bellied out from the underbrush where General Sullivan's advance guard lay. Their fire drove the skirmishers back.

Ohrante clutched Joseph's arm. "Where are those soldiers going?"

The war chief's eyes followed his friend's pointing finger. One of the American brigades had wheeled and was moving toward the Indians' position on the high ridge. Instantly Joseph called in the other chiefs from their posts along the line.

"The Americans will try to take this hill," he told them. "Your warriors must stand their ground and drive them back or everything will be lost."

As the chiefs crept back to their positions Joseph's gaze followed the skulking, wiry figure of the Seneca Red Jacket in his scarlet coat. Noticing the frown on the Mohawk's face, Ohrante spoke: "You said yesterday that you did not think this was the best place to fight the rebels. Why did you agree to it when Red Jacket insisted? You are the war chief . . ."

"Because I need all the warriors to fight in this battle to save the Hodenosaunee. You have heard me call Red Jacket the Cow Killer. He is a coward and prefers to kill cows rather than fight settlers on his raids. He has never been in a real battle till today and he knows nothing of choosing a place for one. But he can make others believe the words that slip from his greased tongue. If he had deserted us he might have taken many warriors with him."

Both chiefs fell silent as they watched the Americans deploying on a wide front at the foot of the hill. Now it was on the fixed bayonets of the enemy that the sun glinted.

"Thayendanegea," Ohrante whispered, "I have sworn not to rest until I have avenged the destruction of my people's villages. If . . . anything happens to me today I suppose I will go to Hanegoategeh, the place of punishment, because I have not kept my vow. Promise me you will try to fulfill it for me, my brother, so that Hawenneyu, the Great Spirit, will let me enter his heaven of Hawenneyugeh."

Joseph glanced uneasily at his friend. "Why do you say such a thing, Ohrante?"

"I do not know, Thayendanegea, but I know that if it does happen you will fulfill my vow if you can, for you are the best friend I have ever had."

Joseph promised. As he spoke a burst of cannon fire on the flats signaled the start of the attack on Colonel Butler's position by Sullivan's main army. Then muskets began to pop all along the Indians' line. The American brigade had started up the hill.

For a time the advancing party held its fire. Then suddenly the whole forest seemed to explode like a train of powder wagons.

On his right, in a glade, Joseph saw an oncoming wall of men in blue. A storm of Indian bullets tore great holes in the enemy line. The war chief saw it waver, buckle, and break into retreat.

He slithered into the open, raised his musket over his head, and gave the war whoop. "Surround them!" he shouted.

The braves fanned out to the right and left. If they could encircle and destroy this left wing of the enemy, Joseph saw, they could then fall on the right wing and finish it off.

The thunder of the musketry beat at Joseph's eardrums. As he saw the jaws of the trap formed by his men closing in on the Americans, his heart leaped in wild exultation. Then, as suddenly, it seemed to stop beating altogether . . . enemy reinforcements were charging up the hill. They were driving his warriors back. He darted up and down the line, brandishing his gun and yelling encouragement. Slowly the Indians rallied until at last they gave no more ground.

Joseph saw Ohrante behind a big rock and dropped down beside him.

"They are like a wall of stone now!" Ohrante shouted in the war chief's ear. The Onondaga raised his head cautiously above the top of the rock. "Colonel Butler's men are standing off the enemy down there too," he reported.

Joseph also peered down at the flats. But he saw something else just below where he and Ohrante lay. With a shout the Americans were sweeping forward again. They came on the run, their bayonets fixed.

The war chief leaped to his feet and ran forward. He turned, facing his warriors. "Charge, my brothers!" he shouted.

In the split second as he swung around toward the enemy again a huge shadow loomed over him. He had no time to dodge or even brace himself against the leap of the hulking American whose bayonet was already poised to strike.

A gun roared almost in Joseph's ear. His attacker collapsed, knocking the Mohawk down and falling on top of him. With a mighty effort he threw off the soldier's body and staggered to his feet. Nearby, Ohrante knelt with a grim smile on his face as he reloaded his musket.

Another gun roared.

With unbelieving eyes Joseph stared at his friend as Ohrante fell, his hand gently letting go of the ramrod that was halfway down the barrel of his musket. The fingers uncurled slowly— it was as if the Onondaga, stretched lazily before a campfire after a day's hunting, was drifting off to sleep. Then the gun fell to the ground . . .

Joseph stood, dazed, benumbed with anguish, until a cry brought him back to his senses: "Oonah! Oonah!"

Overwhelmed by sheer numbers, his warriors were retreating. The Americans were everywhere, rolling on like a wave, driving the Indians before them with their bayonets.

Joseph knelt by his friend's side. He lifted Ohrante's body in his arms and gently raised it to his shoulders. Then he set out after his retreating warriors. He did not look back at the breastwork below. He knew what would happen when the victorious American brigade on the hill swept down to strike at Butler's force from the rear . . .

Nor did Joseph try to run. He strode along, erect, unbowed by the burden on his shoulders. From behind him bullets whizzed close, but he paid no heed to the danger that one might be singing his own death song.

At that moment Joseph Brant did not care very much . . .

After the battle on the Tioga River, General Sullivan's army rampaged almost unopposed through all the lovely lands of the Cayugas and Senecas, in what is today the Finger Lakes region of New York State. The soldiers burned the Indians' castles, their crops, and their fine fruit orchards. Out of more than forty villages, only three escaped destruction.

With winter approaching, the tribes of the Six Nations, save for the Oneidas, were homeless. The people flocked to Fort Niagara, where the British tried to take care of them. Food supplies had been scanty enough to feed the Mohawks alone the winter before. Through this long and terrible one the snow was so deep that the warriors could not even hunt to eke out an existence for their families. Hundreds of braves, squaws, and children died of starvation.

In his distress at the sufferings of his people it was perhaps the saddest time of Joseph Brant's life. And it was made worse by the loss of his friend Ohrante.

In the spring he and his warriors, blazing with hatred for the Americans, set out for the Mohawk Valley. The terrified settlers fled before their advance. Aided by Sir John Johnson and his loyalist troops, the Indians struck ruthlessly at the deserted towns, leaving them in smoking ruins. And although the raiders were finally driven out by an American army, Joseph led them back the following summer and completed the destruction.

Now he had fulfilled his promise to Ohrante, but it was a bitter triumph. Already news had reached Sir John that the powerful nation of France had made an alliance with the Americans. In his heart Joseph Brant knew that the English would lose the war.

What would happen to his people then?

Chapter 15

Joseph's belief that the Americans would win the war was fulfilled by the surrender of Cornwallis' British army at Yorktown in 1781. Then, with the settlers in the Mohawk Valley bitter against the Indians, his people looked to him to find them a new home. Soon after the war's end he made a long journey north to Montreal and down the Saint Lawrence River.

When Joseph left his canoe and came ashore at Quebec he stood for a moment looking about him in confusion. As though in fear that the great rock of the fortress city would crowd them off their scanty foothold on the edge of the Saint Lawrence, ancient buildings of stone and wood huddled close together along narrow cobbled streets that ran every-which-way.

The war chief of the Six Nations raised his eyes, looking up at the frowning rock that seemed to rise straight above him. Grim muzzles of cannon protruded from its sides. Having first seen Quebec when the ship taking him and Ohrante to England had sailed past, he knew it was divided into a Lower and an Upper Town.

There were people in the streets, but no one paid much attention to him, for the sight of an Indian was nothing new to them. Finally Joseph stopped a passing citizen.

"Where is the house of the English governor, General Haldimand?" he asked.

With an expressive shrug to show that he did not understand English, the man said something in French and went on his way. Joseph had better luck with the next passer-by, who directed him in English to Mountain Street, which wound its way up the steep height.

In the Upper Town, with its clutter of churches, public buildings, and houses, its citadel perched on the very pinnacle of the rock, and its high wall defending it on the landward side, the war chief found his way to the imposing stone structure of the governor's palace. In the entrance hall a scarlet-coated officer seated at a writing table looked up as he came in.

"I would like to see Governor Haldimand," Joseph told him.

The officer frowned. "The governor is very busy. He cannot possibly see you."

The Mohawk's face fell. Had the days of paddling through

Lake Ontario and down the endless miles of the Saint Lawrence been in vain?

He drew himself up to his full height, a striking figure in his brightly embroidered and ornamented Indian dress of blue broadcloth, the gorget of his captain's rank at his throat, the eagle-feather cluster of a chief slanting back from his head-dress. Joseph was now forty-one years old. Some of the youthful eagerness of the days when he had first taken the warpath was gone; in its stead was a look of dignity and authority possessed by few red men.

The Mohawk said quietly, "Please tell the governor that Joseph Brant is here."

"Joseph Brant!" the officer exclaimed. "Then you are Captain Brant—the war chief of the Six Nations!"

With a snap of his fingers he summoned an orderly. Joseph waited but a few minutes, then he was ushered into Sir Frederick Haldimand's office.

The war chief had not forgotten Haldimand's stern appearance; yet now the sight of the governor's face, as formidable as the rock of Quebec itself, raised doubts in his mind. Did it portend the failure of his mission?

A moment later the doubts vanished. A smile softened the governor's craglike features as he rose and came forward, his hand outstretched. Looking into those kindly brown eyes, Joseph felt sure that Haldimand would help him.

The governor's greeting was like that of an old friend: "I am glad to see you, Captain Brant! Much has happened since we last met"—his smile took on a touch of grimness as he added—"and not of the best for either of our nations. Now we have battles of a different sort to fight. I must lead the people of Canada to recover from the war, and you, my brother, your people of the Six Nations."

When they had seated themselves, Joseph said, "That is why I have come here, Sir Frederick. At Montreal, when the war started, eight years ago, you said that whatever my people lost of their property in war our great father the King would make up to them when peace returned."

The governor leaned back in his chair, raised his head and gazed out of the window a few moments, and finally spoke:

"It is unfortunate that those of the government in England who negotiated the treaty of peace with the Americans included no mention of what was to be done about their allies, the Indians of the Six Nations. Nevertheless I have not forgotten my promise and I am going to see that it is kept."

He fell silent for a moment, then abruptly asked, "Would your people settle in Canada, Captain Brant?"

"I sat in council with the Mohawk chiefs before I left," Joseph told him. "It was agreed that we would like to settle in Canada on the lands of the Bay of Quinté, near where the Saint Lawrence flows out of the great lake of Ontario."

"I know the lands of which you speak," said Sir Frederick, "and you have chosen well. I should be glad to see my brothers the Mohawks come to Canada. But what of the other tribes?"

Joseph's brow furrowed. "They hope to make a treaty with the Americans allowing them to keep their lands." A look of sadness came into his eyes. "My people would like to return to theirs too, but there is much bad feeling against us in the Mohawk Valley."

Sir Frederick nodded. "I understand. While it is His Majesty the King who must grant the lands on the Bay of Quinté, I assure you that he, too, will keep his promise. Go back to your people, Captain Brant, and tell them it will be done. But first you must stay in my house for a few days and see the sights of Quebec."

Joseph's eyes were aglow with happiness at the success of his mission, but to the governor's invitation he shook his head wistfully. "I would like very much to stay, Sir Frederick," he said, "but my people are much worried about their future. I must return at once and tell them the good news that their worries are over."

In the log shelter Joseph had built in the Mohawk camp when the Americans had taken possession of Fort Niagara, the Brant family had just finished its evening meal. Catherine was putting her two small sons to bed. Joseph, born in 1780, was three, and little Jacob just a year old. Christiania was clearing the dishes from the rude table.

The war chief rose. "As soon as you have finished with the little ones come outside and sit with me, Catherine," he said. "It is too hot to stay in here."

"I cannot come for a while," his wife replied. "There are the dishes to be washed . . ."

"I will take care of them, my mother," said Christiania. "You have worked hard all day. Go outside with Father and rest." She took Catherine's arm and gently impelled her toward the door.

Outside, Joseph and Catherine sat down together facing the quiet waters of the lake. The war chief filled his cherished pipe-tomahawk and lighted it.

He pointed toward the west. "It will be another hot day tomorrow. See how red the setting sun is. It is a sure sign."

Christiania came out of the shelter carrying bowls, spoons, and the kettle in which succotash had been prepared. She went toward the lake, where she would scour them with sand and the rushes that grew there. Proudly Joseph's eyes followed her trim figure.

"I can hardly believe she is fifteen," he said. "Before we know it she will be married—if she can make up her mind which of the young warriors among her suitors to accept."

Catherine smiled. "Yes, she is a beautiful girl, and so good too. It makes me very happy that she calls me Mother."

Joseph heard her sigh. He knew she was thinking of Isaac, who was away roaming the forest with some of the other young warriors. Isaac, now seventeen, had never thought of Catherine as his mother.

"It is so good to have you with us again after your long journey," Catherine went on. "Do you think we will be able to move soon to our new home on the Bay of Quinté?"

"It should not be long. Sir Frederick told me before I left Quebec that he would send a courier to let me know."

"I am glad, Thayendanegea. I would like it if the new baby could be born there. And all the people will be so happy to be settled at last."

Joseph puffed on his pipe in silence. He was thinking sadly of the valley of the Mohawk that he loved so well. He thought, too, of his oldest son and hoped that the new home might cause a change in Isaac. The boy was still hostile.

Just then the war chief's gaze, roving toward the east, fell on a file of six warriors emerging from the forest trail there.

"We have visitors!" he exclaimed, standing up and peering toward the Indians. "Why, they are Senecas—the one at their head is Chief Gyantwaka!"

Advancing to meet them, he recognized the others, all leading Seneca chiefs. He noticed, not without satisfaction, that his enemy Red Jacket was not among them. He returned the visitors' solemn greeting and bade them welcome. The Senecas squatted in front of the shelter while Catherine and Christiania bustled about inside to prepare a meal for them.

Then Gyantwaka, whom the white men called Cornplanter, spoke. "We are very much disturbed to hear that the Mohawks plan to move to the Bay of Quinté," he said. "Now that we Senecas have returned to our lands near the great hill of Genundewa and have rebuilt our villages we expected the Mohawks would remain near us."

As the visiting chiefs lighted their pipes, Joseph explained that he had already made arrangements in Quebec for the Mohawks to move to Canada.

"But, Thayendanegea," Cornplanter continued, "you have said many times that the red men can only be strong if they are united. How can the Hodenosaunee remain united if the Mohawks move to the Bay of Quinté, many marches away? Do not take the Mohawks there, Thayendanegea."

Slowly Joseph shook his head. "We must go to Canada. You know how the American settlers hate the Mohawks."

"There are lands in Canada that are nearer, Thayendanegea."

"We considered other locations," Joseph said, "but none were suitable. However, you speak wisely, Gyantwaka. Tomorrow let us sit in council with my sachems."

The council, which began the next morning, lasted all day. There were many speeches by the chiefs of the two Nations. The Mohawks agreed it would be better for them to be closer to the rest of the Six Nations, but no one had a solution to the problem.

At last, however, as the afternoon shadows lengthened, Cornplanter rose.

"Brothers!" he began, addressing the Mohawk chiefs. "When you sat in council to decide where to go in Canada, you considered only the lands along the shores of the two great lakes of Ontario and Erie." He raised his arm and pointed directly west. "Once in my youth I went with a hunting party into the beautiful valley of the river the English call the Grand. It lies less than two marches from here. It would be a fine place for you to settle."

His words stirred interest among the Mohawk sachems. "Tell us about this valley," they demanded. "Are the hunting and fishing good? Are there unforested parts where crops can be raised? Are there other Indians there now?"

"It was a long time ago, but I remember there were great forests of fine timber," Cornplanter replied, and his sweeping arm indicated their vastness. "Game of all kinds roamed them—deer, caribou, bear, wild turkeys, and many other varieties. Beaver, otter, and muskrat lived along the streams, which were filled with fish. Yet along the Grand River were rich meadows which would not have to be cleared in order to build villages and raise crops."

As for other Indians, the Mississagua tribe of the Ojibwa Nation hunted in the region, but their villages lay farther west. They were friendly to the Six Nations and would surely give the Mohawks their permission to settle there.

While Cornplanter spoke, Joseph sat wrapped in contemplation. He was thinking of the long, hard miles of his journey to Quebec. Upon his return, with the Mohawks' future seemingly assured, he had looked forward to peaceful years with his family, devoting himself to his people's betterment. Yet his people were not the Mohawks alone but all of the Six Nations. Would those who had returned to their old lands be able to hold them? Their only hope, he realized, lay in remaining united for strength.

He knew then what he must do. A little wearily but with resolution in his eyes he rose as Cornplanter finished speaking.

"Brothers!" he said to the sachems. "I will journey to these lands of which Gyantwaka has spoken. If they are all that he says, then I will return to Quebec and tell the English governor we have changed our minds!"

At Mohawk Village on the Grand River the courier who had escorted the tall man in the dress of an Episcopal minister from King's Town took him to a modest, comfortable-looking frame house of two stories set among a score of others of similar construction. A neat path bordered with bright summer flowers led to the door.

"This is Thayendanegea's house," the courier said in Mohawk.

The minister thanked him and went up to the door. At his knock it was thrown open by the war chief with a joyful exclamation: "John Stuart, my brother! When you did not arrive sooner I was afraid you were unable to come!"

The two men shook hands. "It was fortunate that your messenger arrived when he did," Mr. Stuart replied. "I was about to set out on a mission to the tribes in the west. When he gave me your invitation I changed my plans, of course. I am in time, you see, for the dedication of your new church tomorrow."

"I am very grateful to you for coming," said Joseph, "for I know what a long journey it is." He led the way into a pleasant, well-furnished sitting room, calling out, "Catherine! Molly! Children!"

As the two men came in they found Joseph's wife already there. The minister saw a handsome woman with fine features and large, mild black eyes, wearing Indian dress of the finest English cloth, with tunic and skirt of blue and leggings of scarlet. She was sitting with a small child on her lap while one hand rocked a cradle in which a tiny baby was sleeping. Her smile when her husband introduced the visitor was cordial and vivacious.

The little boy in her lap, who appeared to be a little over a year old, also smiled shyly at the minister. "This is our son John," Joseph told him. "We have given all our children English names, but John has an Indian name too—Ahyouwaigs—because he will be a chief when he grows up. Since Catherine is a chief's daughter, under the ancient law of our people she may select one of her sons to become a chief. She has chosen John because she says that of all our sons he is most like his father."

He pointed to the cradle. "That is Margaret, the first daughter born to Catherine and me. She is just three weeks old."

Just then Molly Johnson, who had come to live with Joseph and his family, entered the room and was introduced. She was leading Joseph, now five, and Jacob, three.

"You have a fine family, Joseph!" Mr. Stuart declared as they all sat down. "And what of your older children?"

"Isaac is married," Joseph said. He did not mention that he himself had arranged this marriage to the good and beautiful daughter of a chief in the hope of reforming his oldest son, but a shadow crossed his face. "Christiania is married too," he added. "Both of them live here in the village."

They talked of all that had happened in the years since Joseph had left Fort Hunter. Mr. Stuart, having remained loyal to the King, had had to leave the Mohawk Valley and go to Canada.

At length the war chief said, "I would like to show you our village. But first I want you to meet John Norton, who is doing something that will interest you, I am sure."

As they went upstairs to Joseph's study he spoke of John Norton. "I call him my nephew, although he is not related to me. His father, an Indian, died and his mother, a Scotch settler of the Mohawk Valley, then married one of my older brothers. John was educated and taught English by an officer at Fort Niagara during the war."

In his study the Mohawk introduced the visitor to the tall, intelligent-looking, light-skinned young man who had been writing busily. "John is continuing the work I began with you," he said. "He is translating the Gospel of Saint John."

Mr. Stuart warmly congratulated John Norton and they chatted for a time. Then Joseph and the minister went outside. As they walked along they passed other Indians whose greetings held not only friendliness but the greatest respect for the war chief.

The visitor stopped, gazing about at the houses. Nearby stood a partly completed dwelling. Perched on the roof, a warrior was sawing off the protruding end of one of its timbers.

"How have they learned so quickly to build these fine houses?" the minister asked.

"I arranged for a few white men who know carpentry and other trades to settle here and teach them." Joseph's expression became grave. "There are some among my people who do not like what I did. I have not succeeded in making all the warriors understand that it is no disgrace to work. You will see later where they live . . ."

"You are too modest!" the minister exclaimed. "To see what you have accomplished in two years is amazing enough—but to see warriors working!"

Joseph pointed to a large field beyond the houses. Among its tall rows of tasseled corn more warriors were hoeing. "We are making progress," he said quietly.

He led Mr. Stuart to a stream that flowed under a little bridge on its way to join the sparkling Grand River just below. Pointing upstream to two mills whose water wheels were turning busily, he said, "They grind our corn and saw our lumber."

Then they approached the little church. The minister stood in silent admiration before it, gazing at the pretty building with its tall, slender steeple.

"It is beautiful, Joseph, as a House of God should be," he said as they entered. Inside, all was ready for tomorrow, when Mr. Stuart would preach and dedicate it.

Advancing down the aisle, the minister stopped suddenly, gazing in astonishment at the altar. "What is this, Joseph? A musket and a tomahawk on the altar! And a scalping knife!"

"They are mine," the war chief said simply. "It seemed to me that if I put them there for the dedication tomorrow God would answer my prayer that I may never have to use them in war again."

For a moment the minister did not reply. Then he said softly, "Amen, my brother."

"Mr. Stuart," Joseph said earnestly, "although we have a new church we have no minister. In the old building we have used until now we have had only missionaries who visit us now and then. Will you come and be our minister?"

"I wish I could," the visitor said slowly, "but it is the Church of England that decides where ministers shall be sent. However, I will do all I can to bring it about."

A little beyond the church Joseph stopped. There was a look of shame on his face as he pointed toward a collection of tumble-down huts. In front of some of them warriors lounged, smoking their pipes. "These are the places I spoke of," he said. "But I am very hopeful . . ."

"You will succeed here too," Mr. Stuart said quietly. "Now that the war and your journeyings are done, you can live in peace and devote all your energies to this fine work."

Joseph sighed. "Yes," he said, "I, too, thought my journeying was done. But my people feel that the King still owes them something. We have heard that loyal white settlers whose land and property were seized during the war are asking the King to pay them for their losses. We feel that we should be paid too."

"You are quite right about that," said the minister, "but how does that affect you, Joseph?"

There was a rueful smile on the war chief's face. "They have asked me to go to England and present their claims to our father the King." He sighed. "If Catherine could go with me—but she cannot leave the two smallest ones. I do not like to think of making that long journey alone, yet I must . . . for I cannot fail my people."

In London, Joseph Brant found himself famous. He was entertained at banquets, receptions, balls; and eminent noblemen, writers, scholars, and statesmen sought his acquaintance. King George III and Queen Charlotte invited him to be their guest at the royal residence, Buckingham House. The Prince of Wales, later to be King George IV, took particular delight in him and was his constant companion.

Toward the end of his stay Joseph was a guest at a masquerade ball in the state ballroom of St. James's Palace. With the Prince he sat on the dais reserved for the royal party as knights in armor, shepherds and shepherdesses, gypsy fortune-tellers, friars, and many figures out of legend and history moved about the ballroom floor. The dancers, returning to their places, made a brilliant swirl of many colors beneath the candle-lit chandeliers.

At the war chief's side the Prince said, "What a bore these masquerades are! Since the guests all feel that they must be on their best behavior at a royal ball, no one has any fun!"

The Prince was not masked and he wore no costume. His eyes rested on the Indian's face, grotesquely painted in red and black. "It was a jolly good idea, Joseph, to come dressed the way your people do when they go to war." The sidelong glance that the heir to the British throne gave Joseph reminded him of the glint he had so often seen in Ohrante's eyes when some adventure or merriment was afoot. "But why don't we get out of here, Joseph? There are so many places in London that are more fun than a palace ball."

"I do not think it would be polite for me to leave before the King and Queen arrive, Your Highness."

The Prince's eye strayed toward the two vacant chairs in the center of the dais. "I suppose you are right," he said resignedly. "We shall have to wait till my father and mother make their appearance, but they will not come until the unmasking, just before supper." He glanced at Joseph. "You are always so grave. Sometimes I wonder if you know how to appreciate a joke." He looked out over the ballroom floor again. "Even at an affair where most of the guests are costumed you are getting plenty of attention, Joseph. Just look how that Turk is staring!"

The Mohawk looked and saw a short, portly man in a red fez gazing fixedly at him. "You say he is dressed as a Turk? What is a Turk?"

"Ah," said the Prince, "he is not in costume. That queer-looking red hat is part of his native dress. Although he is masked I recognize him. He is the ambassador from the nation of Turkey to the Court of St. James."

The orchestra had begun to play again and the dancers were going back to the floor for a minuet.

"I do not understand the white men's dances," Joseph remarked to the Prince, "but if you wish to take part I will not mind sitting here and watching."

"Perhaps later," said his companion. "Tell me, have you enjoyed your stay in London?"

"Oh, yes! But now that I shall soon be leaving, I am worried about the success of my mission. I talked with Lord Sidney, the Colonial Secretary, about my people's claims and he said he would take it up with the King and let me know."

"Do not worry about it," said the Prince. "My father thinks very well of you. I am sure something will be worked out."

"You and the King and Queen have been very kind to me, Prince George."

He thought of the many taverns, the theater, and other places of amusement they had visited together at night. Some seemed very queer places for a prince to go. And he did not mention that it was hard to understand why English officers he had known in America considered the Sacrifice of the White Dog to be savagery when in London people went to see dogs, covered with lighted fireworks, torn to pieces by bears.

When the music stopped, Prince George gazed around the ballroom again. "Your friend the Turkish ambassador seems fascinated by you, Joseph," he remarked.

The Mohawk, following his companion's glance, was startled to see the ambassador, still staring, walk toward them. Stepping up on the dais, the Turk reached out and took hold of Joseph's nose.

Suddenly it came to the astonished Indian what it was all about. The ambassador, unable to decide whether his war-painted face was a mask, was trying to find out!

An idea came to Joseph. So the Prince thought he did not appreciate a good joke! Well . . .

With a lightning-like movement he drew his tomahawk from his belt. Then, flourishing it over the ambassador's head, its keen blade flashing in the candlelight, he gave a loud war whoop. Shrieks rang out as the guests fled pellmell for their lives. And amid the pandemonium the trembling ambassador fell to his knees, his hands raised in supplication for mercy!

Joseph sheathed his tomahawk and gradually the uproar in the ballroom subsided as people saw there was no danger. But the Turkish ambassador had vanished.

The Indian chief turned to Prince George, his face as inscrutable as a stone image, but there was a glint in his eye. "I hope," he said, "that my little joke will not cause a war between the ambassador's country and yours."

But the Prince was laughing so hard he could not reply.

A few days later Joseph received a letter from Lord Sidney. *"I am commanded to inform you,"* the Colonel Secretary had written, *"that His Majesty has most graciously consented that the Crown shall pay all claims of his faithful subjects of the Confederacy of the Six Nations which have already been certified by his Superintendent of Indian Affairs in Canada. His Majesty also commands me to inform you that all future claims will be given favorable attention."*

Now Joseph, his mission accomplished, could sail for America with a light heart.

Chapter 16

Joseph returned from England to Mohawk Village in the spring of 1786. For the next eight years he faced an even greater responsibility than that which had taken him to London. It concerned not only his own people but the many Indian nations to the westward whose lands were threatened by new settlers coming into that vast territory.

A new and graver responsibility awaited Joseph upon his return to Mohawk Village. Meeting with his chiefs in the council house, he was told there was great unrest, not only in the tribes of the Six Nations who had remained in the new nation of the United States but among others to the west.

The aged Tahkarihoken, Catherine's father, made a speech telling what had happened.

"As you know, Thayendanegea," he said, "the white fathers of the United States made a treaty with our brothers, allowing them to keep the lands where they had lived before the war. But more and more settlers are moving into the Long House of the Hodenosaunee."

It was what Joseph had feared long ago when he had had to decide whether his people should take the warpath in the Revolution. Settlement by the whites was advancing westward.

"Dishonest traders have come among the tribes," Tahkarihoken went on. "It is only after new settlers move into their lands that our brothers realize they have been tricked into selling them for almost nothing."

As for the western tribes, Tahkarihoken continued, they

were even more restless. One nation, the Miamis, led by Chief
Little Turtle, was threatening open war upon the United
States.

When Tahkarihoken had finished, Joseph addressed the
sachems.

"Brothers!" he said. "The Indians must unite or they will
lose their lands! Now I shall journey not only to the castles of
the Hodenosaunee but to the west, where I will say it to the
chiefs of the other Nations there. It is not too late. But if they
are not ready to listen I can see great trouble ahead for the red
men of America."

The years of peaceful life with his family that Joseph Brant
had so looked forward to still lay somewhere ahead. In the
months that followed his return from England he made a number of long journeys over the forest trails, sitting in council with
the sachems of the other tribes of the Six Nations, with the
Ottawas, Wyandots, Shawanoes, Hurons, Pottawattamies, and
others; even going into the lands of the Miamis near the
Wabash River in what is now Indiana. To all his warning was
the same: "Unite or lose your lands and hunting grounds!"

After a time his efforts became known in Philadelphia, the
capital of the new nation of the United States. President George
Washington sent the commander of the United States Army,
General Arthur St. Clair, to a great council with the tribes at
Fort Harmar, where the Muskingum River flows into the Ohio.

It was held in mid-winter. The chiefs and leading warriors
who had come with them crowded into the fort, straining its
accommodations to the limit. For several days the sachems sat in
council with General St. Clair and his staff. Among the chiefs
was Joseph's old enemy, Red Jacket. Jealous of the war chief's
fame and power, the wily Seneca did his best to impress the
white men with the idea that he, not Joseph, was the real leader
of the Six Nations.

Then the chiefs held a council with their warriors to tell them of the offer General St. Clair had made. It was a bright, cold January day. On the parade ground, which had been cleared of snow, the closely packed warriors sat on their blankets around the central council fire, filling the entire enclosure. Shining down through the blue haze of pipe smoke, the morning sun glinted on tomahawks, scalping knives, and the bright-hued beads on tunics and kilts, and illuminated the wild, high-cheek-boned, coppery faces expressionless under feathered head-dresses.

Standing before them, Joseph thought of the power they represented. There was only one disappointing thing: the Miamis had refused to come. But if he could accomplish his aim and unite these tribes, the Miamis would surely be forced to join.

Looking up at the top of the flagpole that stood in one corner of the parade ground, he saw the flag of the United States whipped out in the spanking breeze. That was what the American colonies had done—united for strength. Now, if he could only accomplish the same thing for the Indian people!

"Brothers!" he began. "The white war chief St. Clair promises if we will make treaties of peace with the United States, our right to our lands and hunting grounds will be recognized and protected. But listen carefully to this: he does not offer to make one treaty with all of us. He wants to make one with my people of the Hodenosaunee and another with the western tribes."

He paused to let the effect of his words be felt, his eyes sweeping the entire assemblage meaningfully.

"Do not be deceived by the white general's words, my brothers!" he went on. "He seeks by this trick to divide us! Then if he chooses to make war upon the tribes of the west, the Hodenosaunee will be bound to remain at peace. The opposite will happen if he makes war upon the people of the Long House. Do not accept his offer!"

Speaking from his heart, he urged the red men to stand together for their protection; and when he had finished he felt
he had succeeded in convincing his hearers to take his advice.

But his heart sank as Red Jacket leaped to his feet. The
Seneca threw a glance at Joseph, his little eyes bright with
malice. In deference to the Americans, whose favor he sought,
he was not wearing his scarlet British uniform coat.

"Brothers!" Red Jacket shouted. "These are good treaties,
whatever my brother Thayendanegea would have you think."
He cast a scornful look at Joseph. "He speaks of uniting—yet
who was it that led his people away from the Long House of
the Hodenosaunee to Canada, weakening our ancient alliance?
Who led us into a war in which we lost everything because of
his bad advice? He does not care whether you lose your lands
by refusing to sign these generous treaties. The English King
will always look after *him!*"

As Red Jacket continued, urging that the treaties be signed,
Joseph wished he had the Seneca's persuasive tongue. Several
times the speaker was interrupted by loud applause, and the war
chief noticed that it was led by some of his own warriors—the
disgruntled ones who had refused to work in order to better
themselves in Mohawk Village. Listening to the approving
shouts that were infectious to others, Joseph sensed that his
hold over the council was slipping away. When Red Jacket finished, a tremendous "Ho! ho!" went up.

That afternoon the treaties were signed with the solemn
smoking of many peace pipes and the presentation of wampum.
Red Jacket was triumphant.

Joseph had only one consolation: the Mohawks refused to
sign. His loyal friends among the chiefs and warriors from the
Grand River were strong enough to prevail over the dissatisfied
ones. But his hope for a great federation of all the tribes in
America seemed lost.

General St. Clair had not only succeeded in dividing the Six Nations from the western tribes; now the warlike Miamis could no longer count on the support of their neighboring Nations. Confidently St. Clair marched west in the fall of 1791 with an army of fourteen hundred men, determined to destroy the Miamis.

Near the tribe's principal village the ferocious Little Turtle was waiting for him. With only eight hundred warriors he fell on St. Clair's force and drove it into headlong retreat, killing and wounding over eight hundred Americans.

When the western Nations heard of Little Turtle's overwhelming victory, they began to be dissatisfied. White settlers were still pushing westward, disregarding the treaty. Word of more Indian raids on isolated settlements and cabins reached Philadelphia.

One day in the spring of 1792 an important-looking letter bearing the seal of the United States of America was delivered by a courier to Joseph Brant at his home in Mohawk Village. It was from General Henry Knox, Secretary of War. In behalf of President Washington he invited Joseph to visit Philadelphia and discuss ways of making peace in the west.

Early that summer, having first obtained the approval of the western tribes, the war chief left his beloved Catherine and their family once more and set out for Philadelphia. He was received there with every courtesy and established at the best tavern in the city.

The following afternoon in the State House, now known as Independence Hall, Joseph entered a large, pleasant office in which a tall man of soldierly bearing sat behind a writing table. The hair above his broad forehead was powdered and he wore a handsome suit of plum-colored broadcloth. But it was the man's blue eyes that caught and held the war chief's attention. They seemed to look right through him, and as he gazed into them something inside him said, "Here is a man whose word you can trust."

"Mr. President," said the aide who had ushered the Mohawk in, "this is Captain Brant."

President Washington greeted Joseph cordially, then turned to a kindly-looking man who sat on his right. "Captain Brant, this is my Secretary of War, Henry Knox."

Almost at once the war chief lost the awe he had felt at meeting the distinguished George Washington, of whom he had heard so much during the war but whom he had never met. The President asked many questions about the trouble in the west, about what had caused it, and about the Indians' complaints. Joseph replied with enthusiasm, feeling that this great man understood. He would have liked to talk the rest of the afternoon, but it seemed he had scarcely begun when the aide knocked and was admitted.

"Mr. Thomas Jefferson is here, Mr. President," he said.

The President smiled ruefully at Joseph. "I am sorry, Captain Brant," he said. "You have given me a clear understanding of your people's problems and there is much more I would like to hear about them, but my Secretary of State is waiting."

He and Secretary Knox shook hands with Joseph heartily.

"Will you use your best efforts to bring about a lasting peace in the west, Captain Brant?" the President asked. "I assure you that I will see to it that your people are treated fairly."

Joseph was sure he would.

During the next two days he was interviewed by a number of government officials, including several Congressmen, regarding the Indians' grievances.

One of the lawmakers said, "It is most important that the west be opened to settlement. We know your influence with the savages is very great, Captain Brant. It will be to your advantage if you go to the country of the Miamis and tell them they had better sign a treaty of peace on the government's terms or they will regret it."

Joseph wondered why he was so interested. Could he be a land speculator? He did not like the man's look nor his reference to the Indians as savages. Politely and with great dignity he replied, "You are asking me to betray my brothers in the west. I cannot do so, for it would not be honorable."

Joseph never revealed the name of the Congressman. But that night, when a furtive-looking man called at his hotel, the war chief wondered if the visit had any connection with the lawmaker.

His caller did not introduce himself. "Certain people are prepared to reward you handsomely if you will arrange a satisfactory treaty of peace with the western savages, Captain Brant," he said. "You now receive half-pay as a captain in the British Army and a pension from the British government, I believe?"

Joseph scowled. He liked the man no better than the Congressman. "That is so," he grunted.

"We will give you pay and a pension twice as large," the man said, "and a thousand guineas—five thousand dollars in American money—immediately."

Joseph looked the man in the eye. "That is a great deal of money," he replied, "but if you offered me twice as much I would not betray my brothers in the west."

The man left, but he returned before the war chief left Philadelphia the next day.

"We will give you more than twice as much as I offered you yesterday," he said. "We will give you land worth one hundred thousand dollars and fifteen hundred dollars a year in cash."

Joseph let his hand fall as if by chance on the handle of his tomahawk. "I am getting ready to leave," he said, "and I hope you will not delay me." His caller departed abruptly, leaving the war chief to reflect soberly that if all those in the United States government were like President Washington there would be no more trouble between the red men and the white.

After his return from Philadelphia, Joseph remained only a short time at his house in Mohawk Village, then took the trail again for a long journey westward. In the Miamis' country he sat in council with Little Turtle and his chiefs. Earnestly he urged them not to keep on resisting the United States alone but to rely upon President Washington's promise that they would be treated fairly.

The powerfully built, hawk-faced war chief of the Miamis rose to make reply.

"We are tired of the white men's broken promises, my brother," he said. He paused dramatically and beckoned to two of his warriors. They came forward into the circle, each carrying a buckskin bag whose contents they dumped on the ground, a few yards apart. One bag contained a small harmless grass snake; the other a repulsive thick-bodied copperhead.

Little Turtle brought his heel down on the grass snake's head. He turned to Joseph. "The white war chief St. Clair marched with a mighty army, expecting to destroy us as easily as I have crushed this small snake."

He picked up a pole and thrust it toward the copperhead. Instantly the reptile coiled, then struck so swiftly that its flat head seemed a blur.

"St. Clair did not expect a deadly copperhead, which strikes with the speed of the lightning bolt, my brother," he said.

As Little Turtle and his chiefs gazed triumphantly at Joseph, the Mohawk's hand crept with a scarcely perceptible movement to his belt. An instant later his tomahawk flashed through the air, its blade a gleaming streak. When it struck, the snake's coils writhed horribly; then it grew still, its head severed from its body.

Joseph picked up the tomahawk. "It is true, Meshekinnoquah," he said, using Little Turtle's Indian name, "that the copperhead is deadly when it strikes without warning. But once its more powerful enemy is alerted it can be destroyed. The Americans have seen your strength, Meshekinnoquah, but theirs is greater. It is hopeless for your tribe to stand alone against them."

The Miami war chief's proud gaze did not waver, however. "We do not stand alone," he told Joseph. "The Wyandots, Shawanoes, Chippewas, and Ottawas are ready to take the warpath with us. Even some of the Senecas are sharpening their war hatchets."

Joseph saw that it was hopeless, but he had one more word of warning. "The time will come when you will remember my counsel, Meshekinnoquah," he said. "I hope it will not be too late then."

In the summer of 1794 word reached Mohawk Village that a large American army under General Anthony Wayne had met Little Turtle's warriors and forced the Indians to retreat. Again Joseph set out for the west. Perhaps at last the wisdom of his warning to Little Turtle had become clear . . .

He found the western warriors camped at the rapids of the Miami River, preparing to meet General Wayne's army again. This time Little Turtle received him with vastly increased respect. There was another council, attended not only by the Miami chiefs but those of their allies.

"You have seen the might of General Wayne, whom you call Sukachgook the Black Snake," Joseph told them. "In the War of the Revolution the Americans called him Mad Anthony because of his daring on the warpath—but I assure you he is not mad. If you continue to resist him he will destroy you."

He turned to Little Turtle. "We are the leaders of two power-ful Nations," he said. "Let us unite and seek to bring all the other tribes into one powerful alliance. In such strength lies our only hope."

Then Little Turtle stood before the council. "Brothers!" he said. "We will be foolish to meet Sukachgook in another battle. He is a chief who never sleeps. And you have seen that he has many warriors who ride on horses and are armed with the long, sharp knives they call sabers. Thayendanegea is right. We must be stronger before we can win our rights."

But as Little Turtle sat down, Bluejacket, a chief of the bold and warlike Shawanoes, got up. He was a warrior of great in-fluence, with a tongue as oily as Red Jacket's. He made a fiery speech, taunting Little Turtle as a coward and stirring the war-riors to a feverish pitch. The council broke up in a wild war dance.

Sadly Joseph set out for home. Due to the strain of his long journey he fell ill and it was on a sickbed in Mohawk Village that he received news of the battle between Little Turtle's warriors and General Wayne's army. Just as the Miamis' war chief had feared, the American cavalry swept around the In-dians' flank, drove them from their concealment in the brush, and cut them to pieces with their sabers. Hundreds of braves were killed, and when the battle ended not a single chief of the Wyandots remained alive.

Joseph Brant's dream of union for the red men had vanished forever. The western tribes lost all they had fought for. From that time on, the great tide of settlement swept westward.

Chapter 17

Time was rolling swiftly now for the aging war chief. A new century, the nineteenth, began; the years of the French and Indian War and the Revolution, in which he had fought so brilliantly, were far behind. He looked forward hopefully to peaceful days.

Joseph felt a deep sense of peace and contentment one October day as he sat with his family in the sitting-room of his home in Mohawk Village. From his chair he could look through the window at the glory of a bright autumn afternoon. Beyond the clustered houses, the forest blazed with the scarlet of maples, the russet of oaks, and the blinding yellow of birches. In the fields the stacked cornstalks looked like rows of the wigwams in which some of the western tribes lived.

Joseph gazed at the houses. Softened by the light blue haze of October, they had a look of peace and prosperity. In one of the dooryards he could see an immense pile of orange pumpkins. At the edge of the village another new dwelling was going up.

The war chief's gaze shifted back to the pleasant room with its fire crackling on the hearth. It was just after the midday meal and all those of Joseph's family who were still at home were there. His eyes lighted with affection and pride as they fell on his wife, sitting with her head bowed over a tunic she was embroidering. How handsome she was, and how beautiful her glossy black hair looked, with scarcely a gray hair in it! One would never think she had borne seven children.

Close by sat Molly, white-haired now but still alert and vigorous, active in teaching the squaws of the village the ways of the white civilization she knew so well. In one corner of the room the girls—teen-aged Margaret and Catherine; Mary and Elizabeth—were animatedly discussing which of the young braves of the village was the handsomest. To discover him, Joseph reflected, his daughters had only to look about the room. But his son John, listening to his sisters with an air of fine scorn for such feminine gabble, seemed unaware of his good looks.

John stood up. "I must be at the playing field in five minutes for the ball game," he said. "Are you coming, Father? We are playing the Onondaga Village team for the championship of the Grand River, you know."

"Perhaps I will come over later," Joseph replied. Unconsciously he passed his hand over his forehead.

His wife, noticing the gesture, shot an anxious glance at him. It came to her suddenly, almost as a shock, that he was sixty, that he was getting old. His hair was quite gray now and there were lines in his face, though they added to the strength and character the passing years had brought to it.

"I presume the girls will go along to cheer for you, John," the war chief continued.

Margaret spoke up. "Of course we are going to the ball game," she said and added roguishly, "though we have not decided which team we will cheer for. The captain of the Onondagas is so handsome!"

When they had gone, Catherine asked quickly, "You are tired, my husband?"

"A little," Joseph admitted. Then he sighed.

"Why do you sigh, Thayendanegea?"

The war chief hesitated. "It is just that . . . sometimes I

think of how most of my life is behind me and that there are so many things I have failed to accomplish . . ."

Molly Johnson spoke up sharply. "Failed! What do you mean, Thayendanegea? You have accomplished so much! I only hope your people appreciate it!"

"I am sure they appreciate it," Catherine said quietly. "You are loved and honored through all the valley of the Grand River, my husband."

Joseph shook his head. "There are still those who are not satisfied," he said.

He rose, went to the window, and stood looking out, thinking of the disgruntled ones. There was no satisfying them. First they had complained when he tried to get them to work. Then it had been because he allowed many warriors and their families from the other tribes of the Six Nations to come and settle on the Grand River.

That had been a good thing, he thought. Now Onondagas, Oneidas, and others, as well as the Mohawks, were able to learn the ways of civilization. So many Onondagas had come that Onondaga Village was the principal one of the tribe; the Great Council House, the capitol of the Six Nations, was there, with the council fire that was never allowed to go out.

And now, he knew, he was being criticized because he had allowed white settlers to buy some of the Grand River land. That too was good, he thought. The white men brought with them valuable trades and skills, which the people could learn. In his heart Joseph knew that in spite of the English government's promises the Grand River would not always be all forested hunting grounds and meadowland farms. His people would need those trades . . . And there was plenty of land— the King's grant ran the whole length of the Grand River, nearly a hundred miles, six miles wide on each side.

He turned away from the window toward his wife and sister. His forehead was furrowed.

"I have not spoken of it till now," he said, "but I have received a letter from Lord Dorchester, the white sachem of all Canada. He says the sale of parts of our land to white settlers violates the terms of our grant and must be stopped at once." He paused before going on with what he knew would be a shock to Catherine: "The chiefs want me to return to England and appeal to our father the King."

"Again!" Catherine cried in consternation. "That long journey—oh, Thayendanegea, it is asking too much of you!"

"I do not want to go," the war chief said gravely, "though I would if it were necessary. But I have reached a decision: I am going to send Teyoninhokarawen."

He used John Norton's Indian name. At home he and the children customarily spoke in English, but he used the Mohawk tongue in conversation with Catherine, who still had difficulty in speaking the white men's language, though she understood it well.

"Teyoninhokarawen is faithful and intelligent," he added. "He makes friends easily among the white men. I am sure he can gain approval for us to sell parts of our lands."

"But you need him here, Thayendanegea," Molly Johnson put in.

Joseph shook his head. "I do not know how I will get along without him. But . . . I have asked Isaac to come and be my secretary."

He paused, watching the effect of his words upon his wife. She looked up quickly, but her placid expression did not change.

"I feel it will be better if he can be near me," Joseph went on. "Isaac is drinking too much. And when Teyoninhokarawen returns from England, he will have all his time free for his translations. He is working on the Gospel of Matthew, you know."

Again he paused before adding, "I have told Isaac that if he is to work here with me he must act like a gentleman or I will send him away and never allow him in the house again."

He was thinking, as he gazed at his wife, of the insults she had borne from his oldest son without a murmur. Isaac's viciousness, intensified by dissipation, had been directed at Catherine many times. His dislike of her had turned to hate and he was jealous of her children.

"Let us think of . . . happier things," Catherine said quietly. "At this season of the year we should be thankful for all the blessings God has given us. If you look for trouble, you know, you will find it, my husband."

Like an echo of her words there came a knock at the door. Joseph rose and opened it.

He found himself looking into the faces of a group of warriors whom he knew to be trouble-makers. They stood there with hang-dog expressions. Not a single eye met his.

"Please come in, my brothers," Joseph said. He stepped aside to let them enter.

One, who stood in advance of the others, scowled and grunted, "We do not feel at home in the houses of warriors who have turned squaw and feel no shame in working. We will say what we have to tell you here."

Joseph stepped outside and closed the door. He did not want Catherine and Molly to overhear.

"We have come from the Senecas' village at Buffalo Creek in New York," the spokesman continued. "We were summoned there to sit in council with Sagoyewatha, the wearer of the red jacket, and many of the chiefs and warriors. The people of the Long House in New York are very angry. With your lies you have enticed many to leave and come to the Grand River, even though you knew we did not want them. And the people here are angry because you have stolen their lands and sold them to the whites."

With fierce contempt Joseph surveyed them. "What right

had the Cow Killer to order you to Buffalo Creek?" he demanded. "Only a coward would do such a thing behind my back. I am the only one who can summon such a council!"

"You will summon no more councils, Thayendanegea," the spokesman replied. "At Buffalo Creek you were removed as war chief of the Hodenosaunee!"

For a moment Joseph was too stunned to speak. Then, with a look that made the renegade warriors cringe, he spoke: "You are more ungrateful than the meanest dog who snarls at those who feed him because he thinks he is being robbed of what is more than his rightful share! What of the hardships I have suffered for you? What of the long journeys I have made to get justice for you? Have you ever paid me one bead of wampum for the time and expense they have cost me?"

The war chief's blazing eyes swept his visitors' faces. "Get out!" he shouted. "Crawl into your holes like the weasels you are before I kick you back into them!"

The spokesman's hand crept to his tomahawk. He turned and scanned the faces of the others, as if seeking support. But what he saw caused him to let go of the weapon. Then, with black looks, the traitors slunk away.

In Mohawk Village, Joseph Brant's loyal people acted quickly to prove their devotion. Sixteen chiefs signed a solemn declaration of their faith in his honesty and his management of their business affairs. Swift runners threaded the forest trails to all the villages of the Six Nations, summoning the sachems and warriors to a grand council at Niagara.

There an overwhelming majority of Joseph's people reaffirmed him as their war chief. Red Jacket's treachery had failed. Never again was the Mohawk's leadership of the Six Nations challenged.

But Red Jacket had succeeded in doing great harm to the Indians on the Grand River. John Norton had left for England.

While he was there word reached London that Joseph had been deposed. Because he was the war chief's emissary, Norton could get no one in the government to listen to his request. Before the truth became known he had left for America, his mission a failure. It was not until after Joseph Brant's death that permission to sell parts of their lands was granted to the Indians on the Grand River.

Chapter 18

The attempt by Joseph Brant's enemies to depose him was not the only cup of bitterness he had to swallow in his declining years. The greatest tragedy of his life came on a summer day when Joseph and his family had journeyed to Burlington Bay on the shore of Lake Ontario, about twenty-five miles from Mohawk Village. Each year a council of the Grand River Indians was held there. It was a time of celebration and merrymaking, the occasion when the government presented the people with an annual gift of clothing and the trinkets so dear to the red men's hearts.

The council took place in a spacious meadow along the lake shore near a white settlement. When it ended late that afternoon the rest of Joseph's family set out for the tavern where they were to lodge for the night. Joseph lingered behind for a few minutes in conversation with Colonel Beasley, who had made the presentation.

As the war chief left the meadow he wondered where Isaac was, realizing that he had not seen his son that afternoon.

Arriving at the tavern, he went up to the second floor, where his family's rooms were. In the poorly lighted hallway at the top of the stairs a figure leaped from the shadows. It was Isaac.

Even in the dimness Joseph could see that his son was drunk. He saw, too, that Isaac held a knife.

"I am going to kill you!" the younger man yelled and hurled himself at his father.

Joseph still had much of the strength and agility that had made him a great warrior. He dodged, trying with his bare hand to ward off the knife thrust aimed at his heart. Then he seized Isaac and threw him to the floor. A torrent of blood streamed from his hand, but the only pain he felt was the anguish in his heart.

Isaac, snarling like a wild beast, leaped to his feet. He brandished the knife at his father.

"Go away, Isaac!" Joseph warned. He drew from his belt the dirk he always carried. "If you try again to kill me I must defend myself!"

Isaac's reply was another lunge at his father. Locked together, they struggled desperately. Meanwhile, several men below in the common room, hearing the commotion, had rushed upstairs. When they finally were able to separate Joseph and his son, blood was streaming down Isaac's forehead. The war chief's dirk had slashed through his headdress and cut his scalp.

As the rest of Joseph's family burst into the passageway, some of the men were dragging the screaming, maddened Isaac away. Downstairs they had to hold him down until a doctor could dress his wound. But when he was freed he tore the bandages off.

Without protection against dirt and grease, Isaac Brant's wound became infected. Several days later, burning with fever, he died.

Beside himself with grief and remorse, Joseph surrendered himself to the Canadian civil authorities. They sent him away, telling him, "You have committed no crime. You acted in self-defense."

Then Joseph resigned his commission in the British Army. The governor, Lord Dorchester, whom he had met in Montreal in 1775 as Sir Guy Carleton, refused to accept it.

Still the war chief felt himself guilty of a frightful crime. He called a council of the Mohawk sachems and warriors and, standing before them with bowed head, told them, "I have killed my son. I wish to have you sit in council and decide upon my punishment."

With the aged Tahkarihoken presiding, the Mohawks held solemn council. At length they asked Joseph to stand before them again.

"Brother! We have heard and considered your case," the old chief said. "We sympathize with you. You are bereaved of a loved one. But that son raised his hand against the kindest of fathers. His death was occasioned by his own crime. With one voice we acquit you of all blame. And may Hawenneyu, the Great Spirit above, bestow consolation upon you in your affliction."

Only then did Joseph Brant take some comfort in the thought that his people considered him blameless. But it was many months before he smiled again.

As though the evil fates that had dealt the war chief so many blows were satisfied at last, the peaceful years began. In the Mohawks' home on the Grand River he had worked hard and earnestly for his people, and had cultivated his farm so successfully that, with the food it produced and the pay he still drew from the British government, he had prospered. He could take his ease now.

Thinking often of the carefree weeks of his second visit to London, he wondered if his gay companion of those days and nights, Prince George, remembered them too. That the Prince, now King George IV, had not forgotten, Joseph was soon to learn.

One day a letter from Lord Dorchester arrived. *"His Majesty the King has most graciously recognized the many services you have rendered to the Crown,"* the governor had written. *"He has bestowed upon you a grant of three thousand acres of land at Burlington Bay on Lake Ontario. His Majesty also commands that I convey his highest regard and affection to his old friend, Captain Brant."*

Only the Indian warrior's discipline prevented Joseph from weeping for joy.

On his land the old war chief built a fine mansion of red cedar, looking out over the beautiful lake. It was two stories, with massive brick chimneys at each end. While it was less pretentious than Johnson Hall, visitors to Wellington Square, as he called it, found it elegantly furnished in the English style, with every comfort provided and servants to attend to their needs. They found, too, a gracious and charming hostess in Catherine Brant.

In these years of ease and relaxation Joseph had time to travel extensively in the United States, visiting Albany, New York City, and Philadelphia, and also journeying to Connecticut and Massachusetts. Everywhere he was acclaimed—as a warrior, of course, but even more widely as the only statesman the Indian race had produced.

But Joseph preferred to spend most of his time by his fireside with his family. Memories of the past were much in his mind. Until then he had often thought that his life had been futile. Now, in the love and esteem his people showed him on his frequent visits to the Grand River and the villages of the Six Nations in New York, he found satisfaction in a sense of accomplishment. He hoped he had lived up to Sir William Johnson's expectations of him.

Actually, Joseph Brant had little idea of how much he had accomplished or of how great he really was.

There were regrets—most of all for the failure of his plan to unite all the Indians of America in one vast federation. As he saw the west opened to settlement that drove the red men before it, he felt that it was tragic that the chiefs of the tribes there had not listened . . .

He was disappointed, too, about the church in Mohawk Village. His friend John Stuart still came now and then to preach, as well as other missionaries, but he had been unable to secure a resident minister.

He wished that his sons Joseph and Jacob might have completed their education. He had sent them to Dartmouth College, headed by the son of his deceased friend and teacher, Eleazar Wheelock, but they remained only a year or so. Thinking of his own restlessness at the Indian Charity School, however, the war chief could understand.

On the other hand, he could take pride in seeing his children grow up, marry, and raise families of their own. Best of all, he had Catherine, his loving and faithful wife, who had never doubted that he would achieve success. And his faithful assistant, John Norton, was with him too, a powerful force for the future in educating his people for better lives.

So this autumn of Joseph Brant's life was happy. But there came a day at last when the old war chief fell ill of a painful disease. He bore it with the courage he had shown all through his life.

On the 24th of November, 1807, in the sixty-fifth year of his life, the members of Joseph's family were summoned to his bedside. Though wasted by illness, the old war chief's face still retained the strength, dignity, and nobility that his loved ones knew so well. Catherine sat close to his bedside, her hand fast in his. Grouped about him were his sister, his children, and John Norton.

As they waited and watched they saw a dimness come over the dark eyes of the white-haired chief. But as his face turned toward Catherine a light flickered in them for a moment . . .

His lips moved: "Teyoninhokarawen . . ."

John Norton leaned forward, his ear close to Joseph's head.

"Have pity on the poor Indians," Norton heard him say. "If you can get any influence with the great, my brother, try to do our people all the good you can."

Then Joseph Brant, great chief, statesman, and benefactor of his people, died.

Bibliography

Battle of Oriskany, The, by Ellis H. Roberts, Ellis H. Roberts & Co., Utica, N. Y., 1877.

Brant and Red Jacket, by Edward Eggleston and Lillie Eggleston Seelye, Dodd, Mead & Co., New York, 1879.

Eleazar Wheelock, Founder of Dartmouth College, by James Dow McCallum, Dartmouth College Publications, Hanover, N. H., 1939.

Feathers in a Dark Sky, by Ray Wilcox, Woodstock Press, Woodstock, N. Y., 1941.

Great Indian Chiefs, by Albert Britt, McGraw-Hill Book Co., New York, 1938.

History of the County of Brant, by F. Douglas Reville, Hurley Printing Co., Ltd., Brantford, Ont., 1920.

History of the New York Iroquois, A, by William M. Beauchamp, New York State Education Dept., Albany, N. Y., 1905.

History of the Royal Residences, by W. H. Pyne, 3 vols., A. Dry, London, 1819.

History of Sullivan's Campaign Against the Iroquois, by A. Tiffany Norton, pub. by A. Tiffany Norton, Lima, N. Y., 1879.

Indians of the United States, by Clark Wissler, Doubleday, Doran & Co., Inc., New York, 1940.

League of the Ho-De-No-Sau-Nee or Iroquois, by Lewis H. Morgan, Dodd, Mead & Co., New York, 1901.

185

Life and Times of Sir William Johnson, Bart., The, by William L. Stone, 2 vols., J. Munsell, Albany, N. Y., 1865.

Life of Joseph Brant—Thayendanegea, by William L. Stone, 2 vols., H. & E. Phinney, Cooperstown, N. Y.

London in Bygone Days, by Kenneth Hare, Payson & Clarke Ltd., New York (no date).

London in the Eighteenth Century, by Sir Walter Besant, Adam & Chas. Black, London, 1902.

Lone Monarch, The, by Guy Boustead, pub. by John Lane, London, 1940.

Montcalm and Wolfe, by Francis Parkman, 2 vols., Little, Brown & Co., Boston, 1884.

People of the Longhouse, by Edward M. Chadwick, Church of England Publishing Co., Toronto, Ont., 1897.

Three Tours Through London in the Years 1748, 1776 and 1797, by Wilmarth Sheldon Lewis, Yale Univ. Press, New Haven, Conn., 1941.

War Chief of the Six Nations, The, by Aubrey Wood, Chronicles of Canada Series, Vol. 16, Glasgow, Brook & Co., Toronto, Ont., 1916.

Index